Born in Tasmania, raise
now living in Sydney, S
freelance writer and lite
Sun-Herald newspaper.
and Canada, where she
political theory, she has
journalist and political

She is the author of three Syd Fish mysteries—*Shaved Fish, Dogfish* and *Sharkbait*—and the psychological thriller *Wildfire*, most of which have been translated into German and French. Her stories have appeared in anthologies in Australia and the US.

REGARDING JANE EYRE

EDITED BY SUSAN GEASON

VINTAGE

A Vintage Book
published by
Random House Australia Pty Ltd
20 Alfred Street, Milsons Point, NSW 2061

http://www.randomhouse.com.au

Sydney New York Toronto
London Auckland Johannesburg
and agencies throughout the world

First published 1997

National Library of Australia
Cataloguing-in-Publication Data

Regarding Jane Eyre.

ISBN 0 09 183503 8.

1. Brontë, Charlotte, 1816–1855. Jane Eyre. 2. Brontë, Charlotte, 1816–1855 – Characters – Jane Eyre. 3. Eyre, Jane (Fictitious character) – Fiction. I. Geason, Susan, 1946– .

823.8

Designed by Yolande Gray
Typeset by Midland Typesetters
Printed by Griffin Paperbacks, Adelaide

10 9 8 7 6 5 4 3 2 1

This book is dedicated to my mother, Joan Oakford Geason, whose love of books inspired me; to my grandmother Dorothy Corbett Oakford, and to my great-grandmother, Susan Latham Corbett Clark.

ACKNOWLEDGEMENTS

I wish to thank A.S. Byatt and Ignes Sodre, authors of *Imagining Characters* (Chatto & Windus 1995) for inspiring me to imagine Jane Eyre. Thanks to Antoinette le Marchant, Colleen Chesterman and Lindie Clarke for that lunch: without it, this book may never have been born. Thanks also to Patti Warn, Carmel Bird and Morag Fraser for their help with the introduction; Suzanne Culph for her good ideas; the librarians at John Fairfax Publications, Sydney, for their help with the Jean Rhys material and Kings Cross Library staff for their unfailing support, and Professor Joan Kerr for sharing her encyclopaedic knowledge of art.

I particularly wish to thank all the writers in this anthology for their excellent contributions to the literature on *Jane Eyre*; Julia Stiles, my former editor at Random House, whose enthusiasm got the project up and running so quickly; Jane Palfreyman, who put her imprimatur on it; and Linda Funnell, who helped steer it to completion.

The extract from Lyndall Gordon's *Charlotte Brontë: A Passionate Life* was reprinted with the permission of Chatto & Windus; the extract from Juliet Barker's *The Brontës* (Weidenfeld and Nicholson) was reprinted with the permission of The Orion Publishing Group. 'From Currer Bell to Charlotte Brontë' was taken from *The Life of Charlotte Brontë* by Elizabeth Gaskell. Finally, thanks to Francis Wyndham for permission to use Jean Rhys's letters and the Walker Art Gallery at Sudley for permission to use the portrait of Millie Smith on the cover.

CONTENTS

INTRODUCTION

WHAT CHARLOTTE KNEW

SUSAN GEASON

Just as Edward Rochester's mad wife haunted the attic at Thornfield Hall, Jane Eyre haunts the memories of all of us who love Charlotte Brontë's classic novel. Jane is, understandably, one of the most popular and powerful female characters in English literature. In an attempt to gain a new perspective on an old favourite, I asked a number of women writers—novelists, essayists, academics, a psychiatrist—to take another look at Jane Eyre—the character and the book.

You might be surprised at the Jane Eyre who emerges from these pages.

The idea for this anthology arose indirectly out of A.S. Byatt and Ignes Sodre's *Imagining Characters: Six Conversations about Women Writers*, which I read in 1995. This book reminded me how much fun it was to talk about fictional characters as if they were real people, to speculate on their motives, question their choices and tease out the deeper meanings of their actions. When I was telling some friends over lunch about the book, Jane Eyre's name came up, and I was struck by the hold that humble little governess had on our imagination. *Regarding Jane Eyre* was the result.

Not all the women I approached to contribute to the anthology accepted the assignment—some had been turned off by having to study *Jane Eyre* in school; some were repelled by its sexual politics and another had simply not been moved by it—but those who did were excited by the challenge.

In an imaginative exercise such as this, any strategy is permitted which helps the reader penetrate the multiple meanings of the text. The contributors to this anthology switched back and forth between the Jane Eyre and Charlotte Brontë windows, speculated about

Jane's sexual psychology, rewrote part or all of Jane's story, changed the point of view, challenged Charlotte's interpretation of events and motivations, judged the text and characters through twentieth-century eyes and even used Jane's story as a psychological case study of an abused child.

You might never be able to look at Jane in quite the same way again. Personally, I find the novel stranger and more complex each time I read it, and each time I take away something new. My childhood memories of the novel—coloured by the Orson Welles/Elizabeth Taylor film version—were mostly of the suffering but rebellious little girl at Lowood School (including the death of Helen Burns, which rivalled that of Beth in *Little Women* on the sob scale) and the Gothic frisson of the mad woman in the attic. Reading it again recently, however, I was more moved by the image of Jane wandering the hedgerows; Jane the bag lady; Jane come full circle, totally at the mercy of other people's charity again. It's not surprising that Franco Zeffirelli left this episode out of his 1996 film version of *Jane Eyre*, which played the story as a sort of feminist romance.

Regarding *Jane Eyre* from this late twentieth-century perspective, I'm struck by the changes in the popular notion of what is appropriate behaviour for a woman. The book was, and remains, shocking, but the reasons have changed. The love scenes between Jane and Rochester, which must have seemed passionately romantic in Charlotte's day, trouble many of us now. We regard a relationship between the older, richer, more powerful male and the dependent child-bride as unequal and potentially exploitive, but in Charlotte's day May-September marriages were common, partly because many first wives died in childbirth. And to Charlotte's contemporaries, Rochester would have been an extraordinarily good catch for a governess.

Marriage was an imperative in Jane's day, particularly for women without means. Jane, who had never enjoyed the comforts of a settled domestic life, had the orphan's hunger for safety and security. Because she was besotted, both by the idea of marriage and by Edward Rochester, she overlooked his self-absorption, cruelty and manipulations. We are not so forgiving. We disapprove of the tests her 'master' subjects her to, and we cringe when she calls him 'sir'.

Jane, where did all that youthful rage at inequality and injustice go? What happened to the girl who beat up John Reed, who stood up for Helen Burns? (She triumphed, believes Morag Fraser: Jane the orphan not only found a father substitute she loved passionately but also won the father/daughter and the lover/beloved power struggles that inevitably ensued.)

Today we take for granted Jane's determination to marry for love, but girls were expected to be far more pragmatic in Charlotte's time. Marriage was a financial contract, and girls were disowned for following their hearts instead of their parents' heads. It's not surprising then that Charlotte Brontë's insistence on the importance of physical and emotional compatibility in marriage—her open acknowledgement of women's sexual rights—shocked many of her contemporaries.

From our post-Freudian, feminist vantage point, what Jane's generation (and many after) would have regarded as obligatory female self-sacrifice looks uncomfortably like masochism.

On a mature reappraisal, the faults in *Jane Eyre*, and in its heroine, become apparent. The use of coincidence jars (Jane's discovery of her cousins at Moor House, for instance); some of the symbolism (such as split oak trees) is heavy handed, and the love talk between Jane and Rochester sets one's teeth on edge.

And decades on, Jane herself turns out to be very different from the humble governess I remembered from my teens—a much more complex and contradictory personality. She's reflexively xenophobic—determined to root out Adèle's French 'defects' with a good Protestant education, to teach her self-restraint and self-denial—and as an unthinking product of the English class system, is pleasantly surprised to discover that the farmers' daughters at the moors school are teachable.

Jane is also more domesticated and materialistic than I remembered. Carmel Bird noticed Jane's obsession with fine things, seeing it as the logical outcome of a deprived childhood, not evidence of self-indulgence and frivolity as St John Rivers implies. For above all, *Jane Eyre* is the story of how an abandoned child, a victim of physical and emotional abuse (and possibly a victim of sexual harassment in the workplace), finds emotional, spiritual and sexual fulfilment in a marriage, as well as achieving economic independence and equality. A fairy story? Perhaps, but also a case study full of vital clues about surviving childhood trauma.

The novel raised a number of questions in the minds of commentators, past and present: How did Jane's childhood influence her actions? What was the 'truth' about Lowood School? Just what did Jane want? Who was the real Edward Rochester? What is the meaning of Bertha Rochester, the mad woman in the attic?

You will find Juliet Barker comparing Charlotte Brontë's education at the Clergy Daughters' School at Cowan Bridge with Jane's at Lowood; Lyndall Gordon speculating about the genesis of *Jane Eyre*; Elizabeth Gaskell recording the critical reaction to the novel and Charlotte's response; Rosie Scott wondering why Jane's early rage and spunk deserted her in later life; Carmel Bird interrogating Jane on the Internet; Morag Fraser exploring the landscapes in which sexual and familial relationships are played out; Amy Witting trying to warn Jane of the dangers lurking in the corridors of Thornfield Hall; Jean Rhys re-imagining Bertha Rochester as Antoinette Cosway, and Jean Bedford rewriting the story for a twentieth-century audience.

Several themes leap off the pages of this anthology—Jane's materialism, her masochism, and the seething sexuality of the text.

Calling Jane's childhood a 'holocaust', Rosie Scott detects 'the ghost of an inconsolable child' haunting the adult governess and the second half of the novel in the way Bertha Mason Rochester haunted Thornfield Hall. Whereas the ten-year-old Jane was able to act out her rage at the unfairness of her fate and the cruelty of her treatment, the adult governess has learned to suppress her anger. In its place is masochism, says Rosie, a 'quiet, seething submissiveness' which makes her easy prey to Rochester's wiles—for whether or not you believe Rochester loved Jane, it is undeniable that he cold-bloodedly tested and tricked her in unforgivable ways—and to St John Rivers' demands.

Given that Jane Eyre was orphaned and physically and emotionally abused, psychiatry professor Beverley Raphael regards her life as a success story. Unlike many abused children, Jane didn't succumb to depression, aggression or an inability to sustain enduring relationships—or eating disorders or laudanum—though the jury is still out on exploitive men. How did she do it?

Sifting Jane's childhood for clues to her survival, Beverley concludes that two women—Bessie Leaven, the maid at Gateshead; and Miss Temple, the Headmistress of Lowood School—were crucial to Jane's self-esteem, Bessie as a mother substitute, Miss Temple as a role model. As well, Jane's sharp intelligence helped her succeed at school and her ability to escape into imaginary worlds through books gave her a refuge from an unbearable reality. While the dysfunctional Reeds fuss and boil behind her, she hides in the window seat and travels, via Bewick's *History of British Birds* to the 'bleak shores of Lapland, Siberia, Spitzbergen, Nova Zembla, Iceland, Greenland . . .'

She also seems to have been blessed with an innate sense of self-worth and a finely-tuned sense of justice, says Beverley Raphael. 'What is surprising is Jane's standing up for herself and the integrity of her views of the legitimacy of her "self" in the face of the denial of her rights as a child or as a person.'

And certainly, from one perspective, *Jane*

Eyre must be regarded as a children's rights manifesto.

It was Elizabeth Gaskell—friend of Charlotte Brontë, successful novelist and wife of a Unitarian minister—who, in *The Life of Charlotte Brontë* (1857), first tackled the question of Jane Eyre's education at Lowood School because of the controversy the novel had aroused over Charlotte's schooling, and the way she had portrayed the school's superintendent, recognisable as the Rev William Carus Wilson. Four of the Brontë sisters—Maria, Elizabeth, Charlotte and Emily—had attended the Clergy Daughters' School at Cowan Bridge: two died because of it, at least in Charlotte's implacable opinion.

Mrs Gaskell tied herself into knots trying to appease all sides, concluding: 'I believe she herself would have been glad of an opportunity to correct the over-strong impression which was made upon the public mind by her vivid picture, though even she, suffering her whole life long, both in heart and body, from the consequences of what happened there, might have been apt, to the last, to take her deep belief in facts for the facts themselves—her conception of truth for the absolute truth.'

But Charlotte never did 'correct the over-strong impression'.

With the benefit of the passage of time and the cooling of passions, as well as meticulous research, Juliet Barker in *The Brontës* offers evidence that, although Cowan Bridge was no worse than many other schools of its time—in fact, in matters such as hygiene it was better—it did have glaring deficiencies as a place to raise happy and health children. Under the regime of one cook (a friend of the Wilson family) the food was rancid and toxic; the site was low and damp; and the practice of making the girls sit in a freezing church for hours on Sundays with wet feet and a cold lunch was inhuman. Though Carus Wilson might not have meant to starve the girls, at the very least he was a bad administrator who hired the wrong staff and failed to supervise their activities.

Rosie Scott doesn't equivocate: she regards Charlotte Brontë's portrayal of Mr Brocklehurst as 'a wonderfully savage indictment of Christian hypocrisy' with 'few peers in fiction'.

After the death of their sisters, Patrick

Brontë removed Charlotte and Emily from Cowan Bridge School to Haworth, to continue their education at home. At the age of fifteen Charlotte moved to Roe Head School as a boarder: she was happy there, topping the class in her second year, and meeting her lifelong friends, Ellen Nussey and Mary Taylor. Charlotte later taught at Roe Head, just as Jane became a teacher at the reformed Lowood School. Charlotte then went off to Brussels to study French and met the love of her life and Jane took up a post as governess at Thornfield Hall and met Edward Rochester.

Jane wanted to be surrounded by beauty and harmony; she wanted to be loved for herself, and she wanted the security of a good marriage.

Novelist Carmel Bird immediately detected the materialist in Jane. Jane the artist notices things as much as people, is concerned with the felicity of her surroundings, and is obsessed with art, beautiful objects, fine furnishings, gracefully proportioned rooms, pleasing architecture, magnificent views. As a small child, even after her dreadful ordeal in the red-room, Jane can still appreciate the beauty of the plate on which Bessie serves her meal, and as a grown woman, clearly remembers the 'brightly-painted china with a bird of paradise nestling in a wreath of convolvulus and rosebuds.'

That's why it is so disquieting to imagine this fastidious, sensitive and proud woman wandering the hedgerows frantically searching for food and shelter. 'Of all the exits and entrances of Jane's life . . . this moment of light is probably the most painful and possibly the most powerful,' writes Carmel. 'It is when Jane, with all her possessions in her parcel, becomes that most helpless and vulnerable of creatures, the homeless woman, the vagabond, the beggar.'

This scene is pivotal because in it Jane lives out the worst nightmare of every unprotected woman—homelessness. Its power boils up out of Charlotte Brontë's personal experience, her rage at the precariousness of women's lives in nineteenth-century England—the fine line between survival and destitution, between respectability and degradation.

When Jane inherits a fortune from her uncle in Madeira, her first action is to spring clean

Moor House then go on a spending spree to redecorate it as a surprise for Diana and Mary Rivers. St John Rivers, who misunderstands Jane—or perhaps sees only one side of her character—is appalled to see Jane wasting time on the domestic arts. 'But seriously, I trust that when the first flush of vivacity is over, you will look a little higher than domestic endearments and household joys,' he snipes.

Stung, Jane retorts: 'The best things the world has!'

Though Diana and Mary are thrilled, St John has to be forced to look at Jane's handiwork, and is grudging in his praise. It's hardly surprising then that Jane refuses his proposal: deep down she wants all the accessories of bourgeois domesticity—a tastefully decorated home full of gleaming mahogany, red velvet curtains, flowers, paintings—not a grass hut in India with hot, scratchy underwear and a cold, scratchy man.

For Jane wants a fulfilling sex life, and she instinctively knows she will not get that from St John Rivers. Jane's soul curls up at the thought of St John making love to her as a marital duty: 'Can I receive from him the bridal ring, endure all the forms of love (which I doubt not he would scrupulously observe) and know that the spirit was quite absent?' No. 'If I were to marry you, you would kill me.'

Jane was determined to marry where her physical inclinations lay, and to join her life and soul to a man who could fully understand her. She rejected St John Rivers because he could not love her the way she wanted to be loved—physically as well as spiritually. Or did she? As Morag Fraser pointed out to me, there's a great deal of unfinished business between Jane and St John Rivers, some of it undoubtedly sexual. They continue to correspond after Jane returns to Rochester and St John goes to India as a missionary, and it's to St John Rivers that Jane's thoughts return at the end of the novel—though most of us misremember Jane's reunion with Rochester as the ending of the story. So in her maturity, we have Jane 'leaving' her marriage and returning to St John Rivers and what he stands for.

Why? Morag Fraser thinks it's the sexual allure of religious aspiration and the unattainable, but perhaps Jane is missing the sparks that fly off the clash of two good minds, two strong personalities. It is St John who pushed her intellectually—into studying 'Hindoostani' for instance—and he invariably treats her as an intellectual, if not a spiritual, equal. Though he might not lust after her body, her mind intrigues him. Jane is unlikely to get this sort of intellectual stimulation from Rochester, blinded and maimed and unable to read or write. And although they talk all day, Rochester does not speak to that deep religious impulse in Jane. There was definitely something going on at Moor House that Jane did not own up to in the telling.

Despite this, it was Edward Rochester to whom Jane flew when she heard the call, 'Jane! Jane! Jane!'

Just what did Jane see in Edward Rochester? On the most obvious level, he was strong, powerfully male (the nose, the horse, the eyes), rich and well connected. She may even have found his sexual experience thrilling. She was, after all, quick to forgive his sexual indiscretions, even to the extent of championing Adèle, widely regarded as his illegitimate daughter.

Even the Evangelical wowsers of nineteenth-century England could see that the relationship between Jane and Rochester foreshadowed a full and frank sex life, and this realisation shocked many of them. Here was a woman writer urging her heroine to follow her heart and a virginal governess openly discussing marital love.

Anne Mozley, a correspondent to the *Christian Remembrancer* called *Jane Eyre* a 'dangerous book' and found Currer Bell's 'impersonations' of women 'without the feminine element, infringers of all modest restraints, despiser of bashful fears, self-reliant, contemptuous of prescriptive decorum.' Elizabeth Rigby, in *Quarterly Review*, attacked Currer Bell's 'coarseness'; if *Jane Eyre* were written by a woman, she wrote, it must be one 'who has, for some sufficient reason, long forfeited the society of her sex.' (As quoted in Lyndall Gordon's *Charlotte Brontë*.)

It was Mrs Gaskell's desire to protect Charlotte's memory from these slurs that made the biographer emphasise the dutiful, submissive side of the plain clergyman's daughter and play down her rebelliousness, her candour and her subversion.

But it was not just sexual fulfilment that

Charlotte was seeking. From another perspective, Rochester looks suspiciously like a father substitute. Jane has never known a loving father: here she has the chance to secure for herself a lover and a father. Or as Beverley Raphael describes it:

> the idealisation by the girl of the older man, master, father, safe and unsafe, exciting, forbidden, belonging to another but ultimately the woman's own—the other is defeated, the father is no longer master, but the partner of love.

It's worth remembering that the males Jane had come into contact with were authoritarian personalities whose sexuality was formed, or perhaps deformed, by Evangelical Christianity, and who constantly reminded Jane of her inferior social status. Reacting against them, Jane gives her heart to a man who values love above both religious scruple and the dictates of the class system.

(Jane would not be human, surely, if she didn't suffer a little thrill at having a man risk his immortal soul to gain her body. It's not only Jane's mind Rochester fancies—listen to the love talk.)

Rosie Scott is critical of the ease with which Jane succumbed to Rochester, her 'humble almost masochistic servitude', though Jane had warned us of her extremism—'I never in my life have known any medium in my dealings with positive, hard characters, antagonistic to my own, between absolute submission and determined revolt'.

In Jane's trials Rosie hears echoes of *Patient Griselda*, in which a bride-to-be is tested almost beyond human endurance and wins through (without a trove of buried resentment to sour her disposition, one trusts).

Fairytales notoriously reek of masochism and reward female passivity, and *Jane Eyre* can be read as a fairytale. Is Jane simply a masochist? Surely only a masochist would so long consider St John Rivers' offer of humble servitude, a loveless marriage and an early death in India? And why so gladly take on the role of nurse to a blind and maimed Edward Rochester when she could well afford a whole man? (Or is this a manifestation of Jane's desire to control her environment?)

Masochism is central to the romantic novel, too, and *Jane Eyre* can be read as a romance, which some regard as a sub-genre of the fairytale.

Certainly, Carmel Bird sees a romantic when she looks at Jane, at her 'willingness to believe in supernatural forces, and her desire to construct the episodes of her life as legends and fairytales, sometimes dark, sometimes light and beautiful.'

Other contributors have reservations about Edward Rochester. In Amy Witting's story, Mary Ann Wilson warns Jane that he seems 'very skilled at making himself interesting.' Jean Bedford, recreating him as an Australian grazier, shows us what he might have turned into without Jane's influence—proud, vain and degenerate. Jean Rhys was 'vexed by the real cruelty of Mr Rochester,' and saw his insistence on courting a young woman and holding a house party under his mad wife's nose as rash.

If Jane hankered after the physical intimacy of marriage as well as the security and social status, so too did Charlotte Brontë, though she had to settle for Arthur Bell Nicholls, a clergyman (not of the sort she had lampooned in *Shirley*, one hopes) rather than a reformed rake. But by then the models for Rochester—Constantin Heger and George Smith—had rejected her; she was alone with her ageing father; and her youth had fled.

But just as Madame Heger stood between Charlotte Brontë and her 'Monsieur', Bertha Rochester stands between Jane and everything she wants most in the world.

Bertha Rochester, then, is Jane's hardest test. But before fairy godmother Charlotte Brontë can step in and remove Bertha (Madame Heger) from the equation, Jane must first prove her mettle by resisting the temptation to run off with the mad woman's husband. (Jean Bedford's Jane fails this integrity test, and pays dearly for it.)

But Bertha isn't only a problem for Rochester and Jane, she's a problem for us. It's impossible now to dismiss the mad woman in the attic as merely a Gothic literary device or a fairytale test to prove the heroine's worthiness to live happily ever after—and win the man, of course. There have been too many women restrained and punished for too many spurious reasons for us to condemn Bertha Rochester out of hand. Like Bertha's brother Richard Mason—and unlike Jane—we do not automatically accept Rochester's version of events: we suspect him of self-interest.

We wonder about the nature of Bertha's illness, but Beverley Raphael says that doesn't matter. What matters is that 'it reflects the then, as now, fear and stigma, dread of danger, difficulties of care, and suffering of those with a mental illness and their families.' But we get the feeling that, despite Jane's rebuke of Rochester when he rails at his ex-wife, the only person who is really moved by Bertha's suffering is her brother: Rochester's sympathy is all for himself, for his missed opportunities.

To be fair to Rochester, though, it does seem that he loved Bertha in the beginning. Jean Rhys certainly thought so. In a letter to Francis Wyndham, she wrote:

> I realised that he must have fallen for her—and violently too. The black people have or had a word for it—'she *magic* with him,' or 'he *magic* with her.' Because you see, that's what it is—magic, intoxication. Not 'Love' at all.

But Jean Rhys could not forgive Rochester for locking the hot-blooded Bertha in a cold, dark attic with the coarse and drunken Grace Poole. He could have packed her off to an institution and forgotten her, however: perhaps it was the memory of that youthful love, as well as his personal code of honour, which saved Bertha from a fate much worse than the top floor of Thornfield Hall—the asylum.

If we question Rochester's motivations in this matter, we must also wonder about Jane's, about exactly what Jane knew and when. Did she refuse to see what was going on upstairs because it would have stood in the way of the fulfilment of her wildest dreams? Mary Ann Wilson, reading Jane's letters in Amy Witting's story, quickly smells a rat at Thornfield and tries to warn her friend, but Jane does not hear. Or does not listen.

After all, if, as Lyndall Gordon points out, Charlotte Brontë, whose life was almost as circumscribed as Jane Eyre's, had heard at least two stories about mad, incarcerated wives, surely Jane could not have been so blissfully ignorant? It's not till Bertha forces Jane to a showdown that Jane allows herself to acknowledge an unpalatable aspect of Rochester's character. It is Rochester's sexual self-indulgence and lack of judgment that stalk the corridors of Thornfield, and everybody knows it. Bertha is the personification of passions run wild, says Lyndall

Gordon: if Rochester is to be saved, these passions must be ripped out and destroyed. And Rochester is saved, reborn through a baptism of fire, a true Christian this time—chastened, remorseful, humble. Defanged, declawed.

The first Mrs Rochester has to be disposed of if Jane is to claim her rightful place as chatelaine of Thornfield Hall, just as Rochester must redeem himself to be worthy of Jane. And because our sympathy must lie with Jane, not Bertha, the mad woman must remain a fearsome fright, an obstacle, not a real, suffering woman. It would take Jean Rhys to make her that, in another century and in another book, *Wide Sargasso Sea* (1966).

When I was a girl, I loved Jane Eyre because I thought I understood her—and I did understand the schoolgirl—but now I'm older I realise I will never unravel the knots in the character of Jane Eyre the woman.

Some of these speculations about *Jane Eyre* could be true, or all, or none, dear reader. I humbly submit them for your delectation.

FROM CURRER BELL TO
CHARLOTTE BRONTË

ELIZABETH GASKELL

Elizabeth Cleghorn Gaskell (1810–65), novelist, short-story writer and biographer, wrote a controversial biography of her friend Charlotte Brontë in 1857, two years after Charlotte's death (*The Life of Charlotte Brontë*, most recently published by Everyman's Library, J.M. Dent and Sons, London 1992). Elizabeth Gaskell's mother died young, and she was raised by her aunts in Knutsford, Cheshire, which was later transformed into the close-knit village in *Cranford*, her popular novel. At twenty-two, she married William Gaskell, a Unitarian Minister, and settled in Manchester, where she started writing novels, the first of which was *Mary Barton*, about the harsh lives of industrial workers. Her masterpiece *Wives and Daughters*, unfinished when she died, was published posthumously. Mrs Gaskell met the author of *Jane Eyre* at the home of Charlotte's publisher, George Smith, in 1849, and later visited the rectory at Haworth. Although she advocated motherhood as a woman's mission in life, Mrs Gaskell was a reformist, whose fiction exposed the contradictions in Victorian society.

TO MESSRS. SMITH AND ELDER

August 24th, 1847

I now send you per rail a MS entitled *Jane Eyre*, a novel in three volumes, by Currer Bell. I find I cannot prepay the carriage of the parcel, as money for that purpose is not received at the small station-house where it is left. If, when you acknowledge the receipt of the MS, you would have the goodness to mention the amount charged on delivery, I will immediately transmit it in postage stamps. It is better in future to address Mr

Currer Bell, under cover to Miss Brontë, Haworth, Bradford, Yorkshire, as there is a risk of letters otherwise directed not reaching me at present. To save trouble, I enclose an envelope.

Jane Eyre was accepted, and printed and published by October 16th.

While it was in the press, Miss Brontë went to pay a short visit to her friend at B—.* The proofs were forwarded to her there, and she occasionally sat at the same table with her friend, correcting them; but they did not exchange a word on the subject.

... When the manuscript of *Jane Eyre* had been received by the future publishers of that remarkable novel, it fell to the share of a gentleman connected with the firm to read it first. He was so powerfully struck by the character of the tale, that he reported his impression in very strong terms to Mr Smith, who appears to have been much amused by the admiration excited. 'You seem to have been so enchanted, that I do not

* Ellen Nussey at Brookroyd.

know how to believe you,' he laughingly said. But when a second reader, in the person of a clear-headed Scotchman,* not given to enthusiasm, had taken the MS home in the evening, and became so deeply interested in it, as to sit up half the night to finish it, Mr Smith's curiosity was sufficiently excited to prompt him to read it for himself; and great as were the praises which had been bestowed upon it, he found that they had not exceeded the truth.

On its publication, copies were presented to a few private literary friends. Their discernment had been rightly reckoned upon. They were of considerable standing in the world of letters; and one and all returned expressions of high praise along with their thanks for the book. Among them was the great writer of fiction for whom Miss Brontë felt so strong an admiration;† he immediately appreciated, and, in a characteristic note to the publishers, acknowledged its extraordinary merits.

The reviews were more tardy, or more

* William Smith Williams.

† William Makepeace Thackeray.

cautious. The *Athenaeum* and the *Spectator* gave short notices, containing qualified admissions of the power of the author. The *Literary Gazette* was uncertain as to whether it was safe to praise an unknown author. The *Daily News* declined accepting the copy which had been sent, on the score of a rule 'never to review novels;' but a little later on, there appeared a notice of the *Bachelor of the Albany* in that paper; and Messrs. Smith and Elder again forwarded a copy of *Jane Eyre* to the Editor, with a request for a notice. This time the work was accepted; but I am not aware what was the character of the article upon it.

The *Examiner* came forward to the rescue, as far as the opinions of professional critics were concerned. The literary articles in that paper were always remarkable for their genial and generous appreciation of merit; nor was the notice of *Jane Eyre* an exception; it was full of hearty, yet delicate and discriminating praise. Otherwise, the press in general did little to promote the sale of the novel; the demand for it among librarians had begun before the appearance of the review in the *Examiner*; the power of fascination of the tale itself made its merits known to the public, without the kindly fingerposts of professional criticism; and, early in December, the rush began for copies.

I will insert two or three of Miss Brontë's letters to her publishers, in order to show how timidly the idea of success was received by one so unaccustomed to adopt a sanguine view of any subject in which she was individually concerned. The occasions on which these notes were written, will explain themselves.

MESSRS. SMITH, ELDER AND CO.

Oct. 26th, 1847

Gentlemen,

I have received the newspapers. They speak quite as favourably of *Jane Eyre* as I expected them to do. The notice in the *Literary Gazette* seems certainly to have been indited in rather a flat mood, and the *Athenaeum* has a style of its own, which I respect, but cannot exactly relish; still when one considers that journals of that standing have a dignity to maintain which would be deranged by a too cordial recognition of the claims of an obscure author, I suppose there is every reason to be satisfied.

Meantime a brisk sale would be effectual support under the hauteur of lofty critics.

I am, Gentlemen, yours respectfully,
C. BELL.

MESSRS. SMITH, ELDER, AND CO.

Nov. 13th, 1847

Gentlemen,

I have to acknowledge the receipt of yours of the 11th inst., and to thank you for the information it communicates. The notice from the *People's Journal* also duly reached me, and this morning I received the *Spectator*. The critique in the *Spectator* gives that view of the book which will naturally be taken by a certain class of minds; I shall expect it to be followed by other notices of a similar nature. The way to detraction has been pointed out, and will probably be pursued. Most future notices will in all likelihood have a reflection of the *Spectator* in them. I fear this turn of opinion will not improve the demand for the book—but time will show. If *Jane Eyre* has any solid worth in it, it ought to weather a gust of unfavourable wind.

I am, Gentlemen, yours respectfully,
C. BELL

TO MESSRS. SMITH, ELDER, AND CO.

Dec. 1st, 1847

Gentlemen,

The *Examiner* reached me today; it had been missent on account of the direction, which was to Currer Bell, care of Miss Brontë. Allow me to intimate that it would be better in future not to put the name of Currer Bell on the outside of communications; if directed simply to Miss Brontë they will be more likely to reach their destination safely. Currer Bell is not known in the district, and I have no wish that he should become known. The notice in the *Examiner* gratified me very much; it appears to be from the pen of an able man who has understood what he undertakes to criticise; of course, approbation from such a quarter is encouraging to an author, and I trust it will prove beneficial to the work.

I am, Gentlemen, yours respectfully,

C. BELL

I received likewise seven other notices from provincial papers enclosed in an envelope. I thank you very sincerely for so punctually sending me all the various criticisms on *Jane Eyre*.

There is little record remaining of the manner in which the first news of its wonderful success reached and affected the one heart of the three sisters. I once asked Charlotte—we were talking about the description of Lowood School, and she was saying that she was not sure whether she should have written it, if she had been aware how instantaneously it would have been identified with Cowan Bridge—whether the popularity to which the novel attained had taken her by surprise. She hesitated a little, and then said:

> I believed that what had impressed me so forcibly when I wrote it, must make a strong impression on any one who read it. I was not surprised at those who read *Jane Eyre* being deeply interested in it; but I hardly expected that a book by an unknown author could find readers.

The sisters had kept the knowledge of their literary ventures from their father, fearing to increase their own anxieties and disappointment by witnessing his; for he took an acute interest in all that befell his children, and his own tendency had been towards literature in the days when he was young and hopeful. It was true he did not much manifest his feelings in words; he would have thought that he was prepared for disappointment as the lot of man, and that he could have met it with stoicism; but words are poor and tardy interpreters of feelings to those who love one another, and his daughters knew how he would have borne ill-success worse for them than for himself. So they did not tell him what they were undertaking. He says now that he suspected it all along, but his suspicions could take no exact form, as all he was certain of was, that his children were perpetually writing—and not writing letters. We have seen how the communications from their publishers were received 'under cover to Miss Brontë.' Once, Charlotte told me, they overheard the postman meeting Mr Brontë, as the latter was leaving the house, and inquiring from the parson where one Currer Bell could be living, to which Mr Brontë replied that there was no such person in the parish. This must have been the misadventure to which Miss Brontë alludes in the beginning of her correspondence with Mr Aylott.

Now, however, when the demand for the work had assured success to *Jane Eyre*, her sisters urged Charlotte to tell their father of its publication. She accordingly went into his study one afternoon after his early dinner, carrying with her a copy of the book, and one or two reviews, taking care to include a notice adverse to it.

She informed me that something like the following conversation took place between her and him. (I wrote down her words the day after I heard them; and I am pretty sure they are quite accurate.)

'Papa, I've been writing a book.'

'Have you, my dear?'

'Yes, and I want you to read it.'

'I am afraid it will try my eyes too much.'

'But it is not in manuscript: it is printed.'

'My dear! You've never thought of the expense it will be! It will be almost sure to be a loss, for how can you get a book sold? No one knows you or your name.'

'But, Papa, I don't think it will be a loss; no more will you if you will just let me read you a review or two, and tell you more about it.'

So she sat down and read some of the reviews to her father; and then, giving him the copy of *Jane Eyre* that she intended for him, she left him to read it. When he came in to tea, he said, 'Girls, do you know Charlotte has been writing a book, and it is much better than likely?'

But while the existence of Currer Bell, the author, was like a piece of a dream to the quiet inhabitants of Haworth Parsonage who went on with their uniform household life,—their cares for their brother being its only variety,—the whole reading-world of England was in a ferment to discover the unknown author. Even the publishers of *Jane Eyre* were ignorant whether Currer Bell was a real or an assumed name,—whether it belonged to a man or a woman. In every town people sought out the list of their friends and acquaintances, and turned away in disappointment. No one they knew had genius enough to be the author. Every little incident mentioned in the book was turned this way and that to answer, if possible, the much-vexed question of sex. All in vain. People were content to relax their exertions to satisfy their curiosity, and simply to sit down and greatly admire.

... Before me lies a packet of extracts from newspapers and periodicals, which Mr Brontë has sent me. It is touching to look them over, and see how there is hardly any notice, however short and clumsily worded, in any obscure provincial paper, but what has been cut out and carefully ticketed with its date by the poor, bereaved father—so proud when he first read them—so desolate now. For one and all are full of praise of this great, unknown genius, which suddenly appeared amongst us. Conjecture as to the authorship ran about like wild-fire. People in London, smooth and polished as the Athenians of old, and like them 'spending their time in nothing else, but either to tell or to hear some new thing,' were astonished and delighted to find that a fresh sensation, and a new pleasure, was in reserve for them in the uprising of an author, capable of depicting with accurate and Titanic power the strong, self-reliant, racy, and individual characters which were not, after all, extinct species, but lingered still in existence in the North. They thought that there was some exaggeration mixed with the peculiar force of delineation. Those nearer to the spot, where the scene of the story was apparently laid, were sure, from the very truth and accuracy of the writing, that the writer was no Southeron; for though 'dark, and cold, and rugged is the North,' the old strength of the Scandinavian races yet abides there, and glowed out in every character depicted in *Jane Eyre*. Farther than this, curiosity, both honourable and dishonourable, was at fault.

When the second edition appeared, in the January of the following year, with the dedication to Mr Thackeray, people looked at each other and wondered afresh. But Currer Bell knew no more of William Makepeace Thackeray as an individual man—of his life, age, fortunes, or circumstances—than she did of those of Mr Michael Angelo Titmarsh. The one had placed his name as author upon the title-page of *Vanity Fair*, the other had not. She was thankful for the opportunity of expressing her high admiration of a writer, whom, as she says, she regarded

> as the social regenerator of his day—as the very master of that working corps who would restore to rectitude the warped state of things . . . His wit is bright, his humour attractive, but both bear the same relation to his serious genius, that the mere lambent sheet-lightning, playing under the edge of the summer cloud, does to the electric death-spark hid in its womb.

. . . Any author of a successful novel is liable to an inroad of letters from unknown readers, containing commendation—sometimes of so fulsome and indiscriminating a character as to remind the recipient of Dr Johnson's famous speech to one who offered presumptuous and injudicious praise—sometimes saying merely a few words, which have power to stir the heart 'as with the sound of a trumpet,' and in the high humility they excite, to call forth strong resolutions to make all future efforts worthy of such praise; and occasionally containing that true appreciation of both merits and demerits, together with the sources of each, which forms the very criticism and help for which an inexperienced writer thirsts. Of each of these kinds of communication Currer Bell received her full share; and her warm heart, and true sense and high standard of what she aimed at, affixed to each its true value. Among other letters of hers, some to Mr G.H. Lewes have been kindly placed by him at my service; and as I knew Miss Brontë highly prized his letters of encouragement and advice, I shall give extracts from her replies, as their dates occur, because they will indicate the kind of criticism she valued and also because throughout, in anger, as in agreement and harmony, they show her character, unblinded by any self-flattery, full of clear-sighted modesty as to what she really did well, and what she failed in, grateful for friendly interest, and only sore and irritable when the question of sex in authorship was, as she thought, roughly or unfairly treated. As to the rest, the letters speak for themselves, to those who know how to listen, far better than I can interpret their meaning into my poorer and weaker words. Mr Lewes has politely sent me the following explanation of that letter of his, to which the succeeding one of Miss Brontë is a reply.

When *Jane Eyre* first appeared, the publishers courteously sent me a copy. The enthusiasm with which I read it, made me go down to Mr Parker, and propose to write a review of it for *Frazer's Magazine*. He would not consent to an unknown novel—for the papers had not yet declared themselves—receiving such importance, but thought it might make one on 'Recent Novels: English and French'—which appeared in *Frazer*, December, 1847. Meanwhile I had written to Miss Brontë to tell her the delight with which her book filled me; and seem to have 'sermonised' her, to judge from her reply.

TO G.H. LEWES, ESQ.

Nov. 6th, 1847

Dear Sir,

Your letter reached me yesterday; I beg to assure you, that I appreciate fully the intention with which it was written, and I thank you sincerely both for its cheering commendation and valuable advice.

You warn me to beware of melodrama, and you exhort me to adhere to the real. When I first began to write, so impressed was I with the truth of the principles you advocate, that I determined to take Nature and Truth as my sole guides, and to follow in their very footprints; I restrained imagination, eschewed romance, repressed excitement; over-bright colouring, too, I avoided, and sought to produce something which should be soft, grave, and true.

My work (a tale in one volume) being completed, I offered it to a publisher. He said it was original, faithful to nature, but he did not feel warranted in accepting it; such a work would not sell. I tried six publishers in succession; they all told me it was deficient in 'startling incident' and 'thrilling excitement,' that it would never suit the circulating libraries, and, as it was on those libraries the success of works of fiction mainly depended, they could not undertake to publish what would be overlooked there.

Jane Eyre was rather objected to at first, on the same grounds, but finally found acceptance.

I mention this to you, not with a view of pleading exemption from censure, but in order to direct your attention to the root of certain literary evils. If, in your forthcoming article in *Frazer*, you would bestow a few words of enlightenment on the public who support the circulating libraries, you might, with your powers, do some good.

You advise me, too, not to stray far from the ground of experience, as I become weak when I enter the region of fiction; and you say, 'real experience is perennially interesting, and to all men.'

I feel that this also is true; but, dear Sir, is not the real experience of each individual very limited? And, if a writer dwells upon that solely or principally, is he not in danger of repeating himself, and also of becoming an egotist? Then, too, imagination is a strong, restless faculty, which claims to be heard and exercised: are we to be quite deaf to her cry, and insensate to her struggles? When she shows us bright pictures, are we never to look at them, and try to reproduce them? And when she is eloquent, and speaks rapidly and urgently in our ear, are we not to write to her dictation?

I shall anxiously search the next number of *Frazer* for your opinions on these points.

Believe me, dear Sir, yours gratefully,

C. BELL

But while gratified by appreciation as an author, she was cautious as to the person from whom she received it; for much of the value of the praise depended on the sincerity and capability of the person rendering it. Accordingly, she applied to Mr Williams (a gentleman connected with her publishers' firm) for information as to who and what Mr Lewes was. Her reply, after she had learnt something of the character of her future critic, and while awaiting his criticism, must not be omitted. Besides the reference to him, it contains some amusing allusions to the perplexity which began to be excited respecting the 'identity of the brothers Bell,' and some notice of the conduct of another publisher towards her sister, which I refrain from characterising, because I understand that truth is considered a libel in speaking of such people.

TO W.S. WILLIAMS, ESQ.

Nov. 10th, 1847

Dear Sir,

I have received the *Britannia* and the *Sun*, but not the *Spectator* which I rather regret, as censure, though not pleasant, is often wholesome.

Thank you for your information regarding Mr Lewes. I am glad to hear that he is a clever and sincere man: such being the case, I can await his critical sentence with fortitude; even if it goes against me, I shall not murmur; ability and honesty have a right to condemn, where they think condemnation is deserved. From what you say, however, I trust rather to obtain at least a modified approval.

Your account of the various surmises respecting the identity of the brothers Bell, amused me much: were the enigma solved, it would probably be found not worth the trouble of solution; but I will let it alone; it suits ourselves to remain quiet, and certainly injures no one else.

The reviewer who noticed the little book of poems, in the *Dublin Magazine*, conjectured that the *soi-disant* three personages were in reality but one, who, endowed with an unduly prominent organ of self-esteem, and consequently impressed with a somewhat weighty notion of his own merits, thought them too vast to be concentrated in a single individual, and accordingly divided himself into three, out of consideration, I suppose, for the nerves of the much-to-be-astounded public! This was an ingenious thought in the reviewer,— very original and striking but not accurate. We are three.

A prose work, by Ellis and Acton, will soon appear: it should have been out, indeed, long since; for the first proof-sheets were already in the press at the commencement of last August, before Currer Bell had placed the MS of *Jane Eyre* in your hands. Mr— ,* however, does not do business like Messrs. Smith and Elder; a different spirit seems to preside at — Street, to that which guides the helm at 65, Cornhill ... My relations have suffered from exhausting delay and procrastination, while I have to acknowledge the benefits of a management at once business-like and gentleman-like, energetic and considerate.

I should like to know if Mr— often acts as he has done to my relations, or whether this is an

* Thomas Cautley Newby.

exceptional instance of his method. Do you know, and can you tell me anything about him? You must excuse me for going to the point at once, when I want to learn anything: if my questions are importunate, you are, of course, at liberty to decline answering them.

I am, yours respectfully,

C. BELL.

In December, 1847, *Wuthering Heights* [by Emily Brontë] and *Agnes Grey* [by Anne Brontë] appeared. Whether justly or unjustly, the productions of the two younger Miss Brontës were not received with much favour at the time of their publication. [Charlotte recalled]

Critics failed to do them justice. The immature, but very real, powers revealed in *Wuthering Heights*, were scarcely recognised; its import and nature were misunderstood; the identity of its author was misrepresented: it was said that this was an earlier and ruder attempt of the same pen which had produced *Jane Eyre* ... Unjust and grievous error! We laughed at it at first, but I deeply lament it now.

... I suppose that Charlotte had read Mr Lewes' review on 'Recent Novels,' when it appeared in the December of the last year, but I find no allusion to it till she writes to him on January 12th, 1848.

Dear Sir,

I thank you then sincerely for your generous review; and it is with the sense of double content I express my gratitude, because I am now sure the tribute is not superfluous or obtrusive. You were not severe on *Jane Eyre*; you were very lenient. I am glad you told me my faults plainly in private, for in your public notice you touch on them so lightly, I should perhaps have passed them over, thus indicated, with too little reflection.

I mean to observe your warning about being careful how I undertake new works; my stock of materials is not abundant, but very slender; and, besides, neither my experience, my acquirements, nor my powers, are sufficiently varied to justify my ever becoming a frequent writer. I tell you this, because your article in *Frazer* left in me an uneasy impression that you were disposed to think better of the author of *Jane Eyre* than that individual deserved; and I would rather you had a correct than a flattering opinion of me, even though I should never see you.

If I ever *do* write another book, I think I will have nothing of what you call 'melodrama;' I think so, but I am not sure. I *think*, too, I will endeavour to follow the counsel which shines out of Miss Austen's 'mild eyes,' 'to finish more and be more subdued;' but neither am I sure of that. When authors write best, or, at least, when they write most fluently, an influence seems to waken in them, which becomes their master—which will have its own way—putting out of view all behests but its own, dictating certain words, and insisting on their being used, whether vehement or measured in their nature; new-moulding characters, giving unthought of turns to incidents, rejecting carefully-elaborated old ideas, and suddenly creating and adopting new ones.

Is it not so? And should we try to counteract this influence? Can we indeed counteract it? . . .

. . . An article on *Vanity Fair* and *Jane Eyre* had appeared in the *Quarterly Review* of December, 1848. Some weeks after, Miss Brontë wrote to her publishers, asking why it had not been sent to her; and conjecturing that it was unfavourable, she repeated her previous request, that whatever was done with the laudatory, all critiques adverse to the novel might be forwarded to her without fail. The *Quarterly Review* was accordingly sent. I am not aware that Miss Brontë took any greater notice of the article than to place a few sentences out of it in the mouth of a hard and vulgar woman in *Shirley*, where they are so much in character, that few have recognised them as a quotation. The time when the article was read was good for Miss Brontë; she was numbed to all petty annoyances by the grand severity of Death.* Otherwise she might have felt more keenly than they deserved the criticisms which, while striving to be severe, failed in logic, owing to the misuse of prepositions; and have smarted under conjectures as to the authorship of *Jane Eyre*, which, intended to be acute, were merely flippant. But flippancy takes a graver name when directed against an author by an anonymous writer. We call it then cowardly insolence.

Every one has a right to form his own conclusion respecting the merits and demerits of a book. I complain not of the judgment which

* Charlotte's brother Branwell had died on 24 September, and her sister Emily on 19 December 1848.

the reviewer passes on *Jane Eyre*. Opinions as to its tendency varied then, as they do now. While I write, I receive a letter from a clergyman in America in which he says:

> We have in our sacred of sacreds a special shelf, highly adorned, as a place we delight to honour, of novels which we recognise as having had a good influence on character, *our* character. Foremost is *Jane Eyre*.

Nor do I deny the existence of a diametrically opposite judgment. And so (as I trouble not myself about the reviewer's style of composition) I leave his criticisms regarding the merits of the work on one side. But when—forgetting the chivalrous spirit of the good and noble Southey, who said:

> In reviewing anonymous works myself, when I have known the authors I have never mentioned them, taking it for granted they had sufficient reasons for avoiding the publicity—the *Quarterly* reviewer goes on into gossiping conjectures as to who Currer Bell really is, and pretends to decide on what the writer may be from the book, I protest

with my whole soul against such want of Christian charity. Not even the desire to write a 'smart article,' which shall be talked about in London, when the faint mask of the anonymous can be dropped at pleasure if the cleverness of the review be admired—not even this temptation can excuse the stabbing cruelty of the judgment. Who is he that should say of an unknown woman: 'She must be one who for some sufficient reason has long forfeited the society of her sex'?* Is he one who has led a wild and struggling and isolated life—seeing few but plain and outspoken Northerns, unskilled in the euphuisms which assist the polite world to skim over the mention of vice? Has he striven through long weeping years to find excuses for the lapse of an only brother; and through daily contact with a poor lost profligate, been compelled into a certain familiarity with the vices that his soul abhors? Has he, through trials, close following in dread march through his household, sweeping the hearthstone bare of life and love, still striven hard for strength to say, 'It is the Lord! Let

* It was actually a woman, Elizabeth Rigby, who criticised Charlotte so harshly in the *Quarterly Review*.

> Him do what seemeth to Him good'—and sometimes striven in vain, until the kindly Light returned? If through all these dark waters the scornful reviewer have passed clear, refined, free from stain—with a soul that has never in all its agonies cried 'lama sabachthani'—still, even then let him pray with the Publican rather than judge with the Pharisee.

[On 28 May 1949, Charlotte's sister Anne died. Charlotte's new novel *Shirley*, was published on 26 October of that year, with the character of Shirley based on her sister Emily.] . . . Miss Brontë . . . had been as anxious as ever to preserve her incognito in *Shirley*. She even fancied that there were fewer traces of a female pen in it than in *Jane Eyre*; and thus, when the earliest reviews were published, and asserted that the mysterious writer must be a woman, she was much disappointed. She especially disliked the lowering of the standard by which to judge a work of fiction, if it proceeded from a feminine pen; and praise mingled with pseudo-gallant allusions to her sex, mortified her far more than actual blame.

But the secret, so jealously preserved, was oozing out at last. The publication of *Shirley* seemed to fix the conviction that the writer was an inhabitant of the district where the story was laid. And a clever Haworth man, who had somewhat risen in the world, and gone to settle in Liverpool, read the novel, and was struck with some of the names of places mentioned, and knew the dialect in which parts of it were written. He became convinced that it was the production of someone in Haworth. But he could not imagine who in that village could have written such a work except Miss Brontë. Proud of his conjecture, he divulged the suspicion (which was almost certainty) in the columns of a Liverpool paper; thus the heart of the mystery came slowly creeping out; and a visit to London, which Miss Brontë paid towards the end of the year 1849, made it distinctly known . . . Before she went [to London, to consult a physician about her poor health], she wrote two characteristic letters about *Shirley*, from which I shall take a few extracts.

> *Shirley* makes her way. The reviews shower in fast . . . The best critique which has yet appeared

is in the *Revue des deux Mondes*, a sort of European Cosmopolitan periodical, whose head-quarters are at Paris. Comparatively few reviewers, even in their praise, evince a just comprehension of the author's meaning. Eugene Forsarde, the reviewer in question, follows Currer Bell through every winding, discerns every point, discriminates every shade, proves himself master of the subject, and lord of the aim. With that man I would shake hands, if I saw him. I would say, 'You know me, Monsieur; I shall deem it an honour to know you.' I could not say so much of the mass of the London critics. Perhaps I could not say so much to five hundred men and women in all the millions of Great Britain. That matters little. My own conscience I satisfy first; and having done that, if I further content and delight a Forsarde, a Fonblanque, and a Thackeray, my ambition has had its ration, it is fed; it lies down for the present satisfied; my faculties have wrought a day's task, and earned a day's wages. I am no teacher; to look on me in that light is to mistake me. To teach is not my vocation. What I *am*, it is useless to say. Those whom it concerns feel and find it out. To all others I wish only to be an obscure, steady-going, private character. To you, dear E—,* I wish to be a sincere friend. Give me your faithful regard; I willingly dispense with admiration.

Nov. 26th

It is like you to pronounce the reviews not good enough, and belongs to that part of your character which will not permit you to bestow unqualified approbation on any dress, decoration, etc., belonging to you. Know that the reviews are superb; and were I dissatisfied with them, I should be a conceited ape. Nothing higher is ever said, *from perfectly disinterested motives*, of any living authors. If all be well, I go to London this week; Wednesday, I think. The dress-maker has done my small matters pretty well, but I wish you could have looked them over, and given a dictum. I insisted on the dresses being made quite plainly.

[At the end of November 1849, Charlotte went to London and met William Thackeray. She wrote to a former schoolfriend from Brussels

* Probably Ellen Nussey.

about the dinner party at which she finally met her literary idol.]

> Thackeray is a Titan of mind. His presence and powers impress one deeply in an intellectual sense; I do not see him or know him as a man. All the others are subordinate. I have esteem for some, and, I trust, courtesy for all. I do not, of course, know what they thought of me, but I believe most of them expected me to come out in a more marked, eccentric, striking light. I believe they desired more to admire and more to blame. I felt sufficiently at my ease with all but Thackeray; with him I was fearfully stupid.

She returned to her quiet home, and her noiseless daily duties. Her father had quite enough of the spirit of hero-worship in him to make him take a vivid pleasure in the accounts of what she had heard and whom she had seen. It was on the occasion of one of her visits to London that he had desired her to obtain a sight of Prince Albert's armoury, if possible. I am not aware whether she managed to do this; but she went to one or two of the great national armouries in order that she might describe the stern steel harness and glittering swords to her father, whose imagination was forcibly struck by the idea of such things; and often afterward, when his spirits flagged and the languor of old age for a time got the better of his indomitable nature, she would again strike on the measure wild, and speak about the armies of strange weapons she had seen in London, till he resumed his interest in the old subject, and was his own keen, warlike, intelligent self again.

A PUBLIC VOICE

LYNDALL GORDON

Lyndall Gordon is a well-known writer of prize-winning biographies—*Eliot's Early Years, Eliot's New Life* and *Virginia Woolf: A Writer's Life*—and most recently, of *Shared Lives*, which was chosen by the *New York Times* as one of the most notable books of 1992. Born in Cape Town, South Africa, she received her doctorate from Columbia University in the United States. She teaches at St Hilda's College, Oxford.

The gripping story of *Jane Eyre* had its source in a bizarre event that happened near Leeds at the time Charlotte was teaching at Roe Head: it had excited much curiosity at the school. A certain governess had married a gentleman employed by the family in which she held her post. A year after her marriage, by which time she had given birth to a child, it was discovered that her husband had another wife. This wife was said to be mad, which was the husband's excuse for bigamy. Charlotte may have recalled this story in July

1845 when she visited the Eyre family seat of North Lees during a three-week stay with Ellen in Hathersage, Derbyshire.* The first mistress of North Lees was said to have become insane and confined to a room with padded walls on the second floor, and to have died by fire. These dramatic details ripened into a story of a young, innocent governess who falls in love with her employer who intends to marry her despite the fact of a dangerous, mad wife secreted in the uppermost floor of his country house. The suspense and horror of the plot owed something, perhaps, to Charlotte's familiarity with the most widely popular of gothic novelists, Ann Radcliffe (1764–1823), whose macabre scenes turn out to have rational explanations. But *Jane Eyre* stands out from many predecessors in the gothic or romance tradition for its unusual heroine: no swooning beauty, no fragile model of sensibility, Jane is a plain,

* Ellen Nussey was Charlotte's life-long friend and confidante, whom she met as a schoolgirl at Roe Head school. Ellen was the youngest of twelve children from a respected 'county' family, Conservative in their politics, who had been land-owners and Justices of the Peace for centuries.

intelligent governess who tells her story with compelling honesty.

Charlotte wrote fast, under unlikely conditions, as she lay awake with toothache and nursed her father in the month following his operation, August–September 1846. The surgeon, Mr Wilson, ordered 'utter privation of light' and 'perfect quiet'. What happened as she sat with Papa in that darkened room in Boundary Street remains in shadow. All we know is the fact that she sat in darkness and silence, and from that darkness and silence there poured a voice that combined the rational coolness of Crimsworth* with the ardour of the letters to Monsieur† and the truth-telling conviction of the 'Roe Head Journal'. It was a voice strong enough to cross the spaces that cut her off from the world. Closing with the faceless reader, speaking intimately from private

* William Crimsworth was the professor in Charlotte's first novel, *The Professor*. Published posthumously, it grew out of her experiences as a student at the Pensionnat Heger in Brussels. Crimsworth was partly based on Constantin Heger, Professor of Rhetoric and proprietor of the school. A gifted teacher, Heger helped mould both Charlotte's mind and her prose, and she fell in love with him.

† 'Monsieur' was Charlotte's pet name for Heger.

life to private life, the voice passed the outward barriers of reserve. The reader was like the listeners in the dark dormitory at Roe Head as Charlotte gripped them with ghosts; now, the reader was to hear a revelation of a woman's life.

For Jane Eyre, Charlotte Brontë turned to the life of the outwardly meek, inwardly fiery governess. Having worked off the Brussels experience, for the time being, in *The Professor*, she turned back to the tales of 1838–41 which had explored the nature and fate of a Miss West, Miss Hall, or Miss Hastings, drawn largely from her own character and circumstance. Jane Eyre evolves as a new kind of woman, based on a more complex blend of herself with her sisters and Mary Taylor.* Mary's far-off life in New Zealand was much on her mind during that fertile month in Manchester.

---

* Mary Taylor attended Roe Head with Charlotte and Ellen, and became one of Charlotte's closest friends. From a Dissenting family, Mary was forthright, independent and practical. In 1845 she emigrated to New Zealand, where she ran a shop with her cousin, Ellen Taylor, returning to England in 1860, after Ellen's death. Perhaps because they contained Charlotte's confidences about Monsieur Heger, Mary destroyed most of her friend's letters, an action she would come to regret.

Mary's latest letters showed her 'in her element—because she is where she has a toilsome task to perform, an important improvement to effect . . .' As *Jane Eyre* gestated in Charlotte's mind, she recalled her friend's sturdiness and self-reliance, ignoring convention, status, and the middle-class norms of comfort to which she had been accustomed: 'She sits on a wooden stool without a back in a log-house without a carpet and neither is degraded nor thinks herself degraded by such poor accommodation.' Here is a model for Jane when she abandons her past to become village school mistress in a simple cottage. Mary was the first to know the secret of Currer Bell's identity: Charlotte sent her a copy of *Jane Eyre*, not from Currer Bell but from herself—a unique gesture at a time when even Ellen was not told.

Ellen, who came to know Charlotte's sources, reported later that she had been a blender of character. There is a quiet endurance in Jane that was neither Charlotte (who took relief in plaintiveness) nor the vociferous Mary, but came possibly from Anne Brontë, the only one of the Brontës to endure 'exile' for any length of time in the inhospitable world through which Jane must pass. Back home, when Charlotte looked up from her manuscript she saw her sisters, each bent over a book. They 'looked thoughtful almost to severity.' Grave and slender, 'both possessed faces full of distinction and intelligence.' So she described them in the form of two studious sisters, Diana and Mary Rivers, who shelter Jane when she runs away from bigamous Mr Rochester. Nor must we forget Maria Brontë who lives on in the shape of the transcendent Helen Burns, Jane's first model—unlike Jane in self-abnegation, yet a profound influence for resolute integrity. The flat exemplars of the past, the stainless saints and the good dying children of Evangelical tales, fade before the palpable impact of her living, aspiring, failing breath. Later, when critics questioned the perfection of Helen Burns' character, Charlotte insisted that she was 'real enough. I have exaggerated nothing there. I abstained from recording much that I remembered respecting her, lest the narrative should sound incredible.'

Though Charlotte drew on actual women in order to create a new figure, she had to imagine circumstances in which such a creature might be driven to emerge from the shadow of the mind on to the platform of action—not, as Mary, in some remote outpost of empire, but in the placid drawing-rooms and repressive schools of the north of England. The transit from life to invention is a shift from one kind of truth to another. Which, we might ask, is better: documentary or imaginative truth, fact or fiction? Jane Eyre is too honest, dauntless, and ultimately too fortunate to exist in nineteenth-century England; she is a creative truth: not woman as she is, but as she might be. As potential exemplar, Jane sets before us her trials and possibilities.

Jane Eyre is, above all, a pilgrimage. It follows child and woman through pitfalls en route to her new Eden: a love which unites goodness with the dream of sustained passion. In this new map for the soul, the Fall is not disobedience; it is obedience—unthinking obedience. Mrs Reed, Jane's guardian aunt, complains that she has never seen a child like her. What sets Jane apart is that she is incapable of not thinking for herself; the brutal acts of repression in the Reed household happen because Jane thinks, and also because, as a child, she blurts out what she thinks with blunt acumen: '*Speak* I must . . .' A full-formed speech pours out in self-defence against misrepresentation, and at this, Jane feels her soul begin to expand 'with the strangest sense of freedom, of triumph, I ever felt. It seemed as if an invisible bond had burst . . .' As Jane grows, she learns that she may not use language in this way: she must mute truth and mediate it through the low voice of schooled politeness, but the search for truth goes on.

In her journey through a social world, the temptation to fall is ever present in a variety of plausible forms. Jane is lost should she once succumb to any of the plots on offer. There is the plot for the dependent orphan whom the Reeds would fix in her place as poor relation. There is the plot for the charity girl whom Lowood would fix in postures of humility, leading to servitude of the upper classes. There is the plot for a grown-up Jane, devised by a married gentleman: to be his mistress in a Mediterranean hideaway where Rochester, according to habit, would confer sultan smiles, erotic stupefactions, and material rewards. Finally, there is the most plausible plot of all, traditional marriage, on offer from that figure of marble beauty and impeccable rectitude, St John Rivers: the temptation of the mature Jane to come under the sway of an egotistical missionary. Can she distinguish the valid demands of altruism from the cant of sacrifice which tempts her to lose her life—worse, to lose her very self—in distant service to pure principle, unwarmed by any concession to human need?

These plots, the pilgrim must see for the played-out fictions they are: all are posited on a false premiss about women's nature as biddable and inferior. The pioneer of a new Progress must break through the encrustations of language, lover's and religious cant, to see, to *see* in the sense of revelation, the destructive self-interest of persons in positions of power. As Christian once did battle with Obstinate or the Giant Despair, so Jane must outface the deceptive faces of nineteenth-century Benevolence. Mrs Reed, the Revd Mr Brocklehurst, Mr Rochester, and the Revd Mr Rivers believe themselves benefactors. For Jane to succumb to Mrs Reed, to the founder of the charity school, to her lover (in his sultan aspect), or to her apparent saviour, would be to lose her soul. When Rochester, thwarted in his bigamous plan, pleads with Jane to live with him, if only to keep him from 'lust', 'vice', and 'despair', she is tempted to 'save him'. When he asks her to transgress 'a mere human law', Conscience and Reason turn traitors against her and Feeling clamours:

> 'Who in the world cares for *you*? or who will be injured by what you do?'
>
> Still indomitable was the reply—'*I* care for myself.'

This indomitable '*I*' sustains her through the scene that follows, when Rochester seizes her physically—physically, she is powerless, as Rochester, driven by possessive fury, allows himself to lose control. Her eye meets his devouring glance and calls him back to what she is: '—mentally, I still possessed my soul, and with it the certainty of ultimate safety.'

Many have criticised Jane for her resistance. Mary Ann Evans (later, George Eliot) wrote to Charles Bray on 11 June 1848:

> All self-sacrifice is good—but one would like it to be in a somewhat nobler cause than that of a diabolical law which chains a man soul and body to a putrefying carcase.

Eventually, when Miss Evans chose to live with George Henry Lewes, who was locked in a licentious marriage, she did not require a legal tie in circumstances which made this impossible. This is Rochester's line, and he reproaches Jane for her 'difficult' nature—'flinty', Jane agrees. Morals apart, her 'difficulty' is that she cannot put herself in the power of a man who has used her untruthfully. Passionate as she is, she cannot be subdued to stale schemes of seduction which lead to the weak position of a mistress. In retrospect Elizabeth Hastings' denial of her loved seducer was a rehearsal for this supremely difficult renunciation.

Jane charts her Progress through a world in which gains are precarious, while danger threatens almost to the end. The pilgrim must retain her clarity at all costs—her keen awareness of injustice and the exploitation masked as benevolence—but she must see all this without that rage she had known as a child, screaming and beating on the door when she was locked in the red-room until frenzy collapsed into illness. That early extravagance teaches her to track a middle course: to gain knowledge without capitulation to the regimented aspect of schooling; to retain strength of feeling without capitulation to licence; to become self-sufficient and economically independent without a chilling degree of purpose. If she is to survive, she cannot afford, either, to succumb to the internal temptations of despair, when she is locked in the red-room, when she is humiliated at school, and—most difficult—when she cannot marry Mr Rochester.

To follow such a course requires more strength than was usually allowed women in the nineteenth century. In short, such a course could only proceed on a novel premiss about the nature of the 'weaker sex'. This was derived from Charlotte's discoveries about herself, her sisters, and friends, and it was the heat of these discoveries that made the book so revolutionary to its time and ours. 'The standard heroes and heroines of novels are personages ... whom I could never ... believe to be natural, or wish to imitate.' When Charlotte Brontë theorised, her appeal was to Nature:

> Were I obliged to copy any former novelist, even the greatest, even Scott ... I would not write ... Unless I can look beyond the greatest Masters, and study Nature herself, I have no right to paint. Unless I have the courage to use the language of

> Truth in preference to the jargon of Conventionality, I ought to be silent.

Rochester shares the language of truth. He, alone, has the insight to know Jane, and the confidence to encourage her to be what she is: 'An unusual—to me—a perfectly new character I suspected was yours: I desired to search it deeper, and know it better.' This had been validated by Monsieur's capacity to know Charlotte; in fact, Rochester's words to Jane are close to Heger's style:

> 'You entered the room with a look and air at once shy and independent ... I made you talk: ere long I found you full of strange contrasts. Your garb and manner are restricted by rule ... yet, when addressed, you lifted a keen, a daring, and a glowing eye ... there was penetration and power in each glance you gave ...'

At length, he perceives that what he is seeing has the permanent stamp of nature. It 'was no transitory blossom; but rather the radiant resemblance of one, cut in an indestructible gem.'

As new-found creature, Jane will not permit

any lapse into reductive terms. When Rochester casts Jane as comforting angel, she laughs at him:

> 'I am not an angel,' I asserted; 'and I will not be one till I die: I will be myself. Mr Rochester, you must neither expect nor exact anything celestial of me, for you will not get it, any more than I shall get it of you; which I do not at all anticipate.'

When Rochester calls his mad wife 'that demon ... that fearful hag,' Jane will, again, refuse his language:

> 'Sir,' I interrupted him, 'you are inexorable for that unfortunate lady: you speak of her with hate—with vindictive antipathy. It is cruel—she cannot help being mad.'

The reductive view that Jane resists is rooted in theology with its categorisation of women as saints or sinners. Unlike Jane, Charlotte herself was not exempt from the glib phrase that guarded her self-protective distance and carefully preserved gentility when she took the view that Branwell was a lost soul. Emily, unconcerned with refinement, could afford to pity Branwell, to see a Fall, not a demon.

Emily went further than her sister in questioning the codes and language of religion, with her assault on heaven, dogmatism, and false humility. Organised religion has held the monopoly on souls; Emily reclaimed them.

... Charlotte had more in her of the social concerns of the Old Testament prophet; Emily more of the New Testament reach beyond death. Emily practised a loneliness that Byron at times felt but could not live with and could not purify:

> From my youth
> My spirit walk'd not with the souls of men,
> Nor look'd upon the earth with human eyes.

She shed plots more ruthlessly than Charlotte, the 'hope of youth' and 'fancy's rainbow', for what she called 'infinity'. Like her admirer, Emily Dickinson, she lived for a rising life beyond death.

Charlotte would not concede the impossibility of sustained passion within this world. Jane Eyre will not settle for anything beyond or less than a transformed Rochester. He is the educable man. Though blinded in the fire that destroys his wife, he can learn to 'see' his true mate who is not to be his grateful dependant but his equal. Rochester rides out of darkness, and is largely a creation in the dark. His appearance—whether ugly or not—is irrelevant because what Jane sees is his promise to know *her*. This knowing is blocked, to some extent, by sultan habits (the wrong sort of masterfulness which presumes to think for her, in fact to trick her into false union). Rochester must learn to see Jane's right to her integrity: this 'seeing' is a triumph, not a loss. To deride Rochester as an impossible dream is to misread Charlotte Brontë. She was a reformer. Where Emily terminates in 'infinity', Charlotte is closer to contemporaries like Dickens and Mrs Gaskell who look to a society improved through reformed characters. Rochester is not meant to represent men as they were, but a man as he might be.

Charlotte Brontë denied any identity with Jane beyond plainness. With contemporaries, it was prudent to preserve her detachment from that passionate voice. In fact, the author had not the overt rage nor quite the unflinching strength of Jane. But her story sets out an exemplary pattern which realises the deepest structure of

Charlotte's own life. The subtitle, *An Autobiography*, is true, not in the literal way that *The Professor* drew on events in the author's life, but in its polarities: the tensions of pilgrimage and passion, of chill and fire, the iron grip of rational control and the anarchic abandon that Charlotte had known in the shadow of Branwell. 'The action of the tale is sometimes unnatural,' said a reviewer, 'but the passion is always true.' 'It is an autobiography,' said George Henry Lewes in *Fraser's Magazine*, '—not, perhaps, in the naked facts and circumstances, but in the actual suffering and experience.'

Autobiography is an attempt to distil from the life a form and meaning. Charlotte's letters to Ellen and Monsieur insist on her atrophy in Haworth, her loss of her '*maître*', and her despair over 'doing nothing yet' at nearly thirty, at nearly thirty-one. And to Ellen she confides, too, the impossibility of marriage: the men she met in West Yorkshire were either 'narrow' curates or worldly cynics like Mary's brother, Joe, who demanded looks and means when they came to marry. No Englishman she encountered could have conceived of knowing a woman in the way she wished, or could have said those liberating words that Rochester says to Jane: '... in time, I think you will learn to be natural with me, as I find it impossible to be conventional with you'.

It would be easy to dwell on futility and sadness, yet this would not explain Currer Bell's command: her will to convert life into meaning. *Jane Eyre* selects for those trials that emerge as gains. The loss of Maria, retold through Helen Burns, is an instructive episode in a Progress. The loss of Monsieur and the ensuing depression drives Jane into the wilderness near Whitcross. Her gain is Charlotte's in the aftermath of Brussels: a determined endurance, dramatised in the final volume where Jane must part with Rochester to devise another fate. Whitcross was derived from the stone pillar known as the Moscar Cross, close to the Hallam moors in Derbyshire which Charlotte would have seen when she vacationed with Ellen in the village of Hathersage in the summer of 1845. The pillar marked the crossroads where the old east-west road from Sheffield to Manchester crossed the north-south road from Yorkshire. It might be said to mark a moment, a year and a half after Charlotte's flight from Monsieur, when she conceived for herself a new story.

In *Jane Eyre*, Currer Bell found ways of dramatising desires and principles, so as to speak to all readers, not only women. Through the hidden alien in all women we discover the singularity of all members of our species and beyond this, our dualities, our plural languages, beyond the horizon on Jane's repeated gaze, beyond sight. One reviewer, William George Clark, hearing extravagant praise, resolved to be 'as critical as Croker'. But as he read on, he forgot commendations and criticism, identified with Jane in all her troubles, 'and finally married Mr Rochester about four in the morning.' What carries the reader, as Lewes recognised, is the book's voice: 'it is soul speaking to soul; it is an utterance from the depths of a struggling, suffering, much-enduring spirit: *suspiria de profundis*!'

Though Charlotte Brontë wrote at the onset of a long and still-advancing period when women must question the abuses of power—sexual power, violence, militarism, and the evils these perpetuate—from an objective distance, men and women belong to the same species, sharing the same fundamental pattern of existence. Have we attractions as a species, we might well ask, and shall we go on? Jane, as survivor, with unflinching moral courage, reason in command of passion, and vigour which derives from vivacity of mind, embodies a principled resilience all can share. As orphan, she stands for all who are dependent and alone, who are vulnerable to abuse, both crass abuse of child, class, or woman, and also that more subtle abuse explored in all Charlotte Brontë's work: denial of feeling.

The bully, John Reed, cuffs Jane because she will not show him due deference. Brocklehurst humiliates Jane, and starves the girls at Lowood in order to break their spirit; but, when Jane looks back, it is his words—repressive, threatening, sanctimonious words—that remain the focus of resentment. What draws Jane to Rochester, despite his dubious past, his growls, and gloom, is that Rochester invites the opposite of this denial: 'I have not been petrified', Jane tells him when she explains her attachment. 'I have not been buried with inferior minds, and excluded from every glimpse of communion with what is bright, and energetic, and high.'

In contrast, Mr Brocklehurst and St John Rivers are pillars of a structure that denied the right of feeling to those it designed for service.

The danger of this emotional imprisonment is the depletion of character, as Anne Brontë feared when she went 'flat' after her years with the Robinsons, or as Jane fears when Mr Rivers (saying 'I . . . I . . . I . . .') insists on marriage to support his spiritual ambition.

Jane and Rochester both pass through their periods in the wilderness: Jane begging for food and shelter near Whitcross; Rochester a blind recluse at Ferndean, after the fire that destroys his house. Jane's self-reliance is tested under conditions of extremity when she is bereft of protection, money, the means for cleanliness, even the reserve dear to her pride. Rochester, in turn, is stripped of the sultan aspect of power—the power that had charmed the parasites (Céline, Giacinta, and Clara) of his licentious past. Sultan largesse had been an irritant to Jane: it would make her a ridiculous doll. Worse, it had presumed to think for her, to plan a false wedding: '. . . I would not say he had betrayed me: but the attribute of stainless truth was gone from his idea; and from his presence I must go'. Yet all that is desirable in Rochester's power does survive this parting and their subsequent ordeals. Still retrievable beneath his encrustations of bitterness are his knowing, his verbal play, his ready engagement with Jane. The final chapter, which follows the pair through the first years of their marriage, asserts the success of sustained compatibility: 'We talk, I believe, all day long'.

This resolution of freedom and bonding comes about only when Jane has purged herself finally of two forms of tyranny. First, she must free herself of the tyranny of licence: the child's abandon to rage, and the adult's abandon to appetite that leads to the concealed frenzy in Rochester's home, Thornfield Hall.

Bertha Mason Rochester, the mad woman on the third floor, is a warning more than a character: a warning of mindless passion. Jane veers closest to her in one cancelled sentence in the manuscript which admits an underlying recklessness in her susceptibility to Rochester during their engagement: '... if he was subjugated so was I—and that by a strange and resistless sway'. This is checked after the disclosure of attempted bigamy, followed by the visit to Rochester's mad wife. Jane, alone in her room, stops the momentum of shared passion with the words (heavily under-scored in the manuscript), 'but *now—I thought*.' Her reassertion of reason separates her sharply from the madness in which Rochester continues to remain implicated. Bertha embodies the anarchic element in Rochester, rampant until she is dead. Dying in her blaze of fire, she leaves him scarred and, to a degree, disabled. It is suggestive that it is Rochester she disables, not Jane. He has been scarred by his part in a long tradition of flawed judgment. For Bertha Mason never was a promising woman; she was thick, with slow, unmoving eyes, like those of her brother.

The creative madness that Charlotte Brontë and other writers—Emily Dickinson, Olive Schreiner, Virginia Woolf, Sylvia Plath—experienced, in one way or another, is different from the vicious madness of Bertha. She is stupidly violent, like capricious fighter dogs with rending teeth. As Charlotte Brontë conceived her, Bertha was the cause of her misfortune, not her husband. It will not do to infuse Bertha with feminist sentiment if we care at all for what is there on the page as an emanation of its time and place. I see it as part of Charlotte Brontë's greatness that she will not simplify truth as truism. Women are not simply victims; they have, within them, the agency to discover gains in the most restrictive life. That is what Charlotte sought to show.

Bertha is not to be aligned with such able, suppressed women, rather with the showy female type Charlotte deplored: the rich, thick, insensitive beauties. Men trail after them, abandoning their better natures to lust and greed, as Rochester degraded himself through his union with Bertha. She is most threatening as a relic of dangers in Rochester's nature, hidden and for a long time unknown to Jane, who finds herself susceptible to a man who has accustomed himself to the shallowness that can treat a succession of bodies as passing pleasure. This is what Bertha means as Rochester's mate, a part of him that may be invisible but lives on. Rochester travels between passion in its debased form and passion as he knows it with Jane, which can redeem and heal him because (he sees as he reads her face) it has the grace of reason.

Rochester occupies an ambiguous position. In part he represents the traditional man who constructs 'woman' as opposite and alien, a defective 'other' to be shut away if he is to assert his autonomous existence. To relegate Bertha to a separate region of the house is to deny some part of himself, a bestial lust and rage, which he expels beyond the domestic boundary he must police with strict rules—unsuccessfully, for Bertha is liable to break out and invade her husband's bedroom with furious incendiary attentions. And yet Rochester is also a man who can learn to cultivate the 'other' in the form of Jane whom he comes to recognise as his better self. He can promote genuine knowledge of this alien 'sprite'. Confident in his manhood, he can admit the 'other' to intimacy, but he can do so only by a love that confronts his controlling habits of force and lust.

The tyranny of licence is no more dangerous than the tyranny of self-constriction, that denial of the right to feeling that Mr Brocklehurst and St John Rivers seek to impose through their brands of religion. To succumb to Rivers with his high-flown discourse of sacrifice would be, Jane sees, to lose half her self. She prays in a different way to St John's, but effective in its own fashion. As Jane had claimed her right of communication with what is bright, energetic, high, so, with Rivers, she claims what Helen Burns had practised, a religion of her own. The real daring of this book lies not in Jane's moments of anger and rebellion, nor in the loveplay of Jane and Rochester, nor even in replacing cant with a purer Christianity, but in Jane's claim to think for herself—not only as a woman and worker but as a spirit equal to any other spirit, and with the same right to exist and experience:

> '—I have as much soul as you, [Jane tells Rochester]—and full as much heart! ... I am not talking to you now through the medium of custom, conventionalities, nor even of mortal flesh: —it is my spirit that addresses your spirit; just as if both had passed through the grave, and we stood at God's feet, equal, —as we are!'

Part of Jane's experience is to know the extremes of a seething, chaotic life and one of disciplined order. It is here that Charlotte Brontë gave form and meaning to the private extravagance of her own life tugged between the claims of the self and the claims of society. Here is the 'inner strife' that Virginia Woolf perceived in Currer Bell and George Eliot—and presumably in her own 'night and day'. To what extent Charlotte Brontë resolved the 'inner strife' remains to be seen; but Currer Bell lays down the path of resolution in 1846–47 as she follows Jane Eyre in her transitions from the restrictive Lowood to the tempestuous Thornfield, and from Thornfield to the bare testing-ground of Whitcross, to her final habitation in the fertile landscape of Ferndean where the broken hall, inhabited by a damaged Rochester, might be restored. In the course of her journeys, Jane learns to guard herself against the excesses of heat and frigid self-discipline. These extremes are embodied in two men: Rochester who offers passion without marriage, and Rivers who offers marriage without passion.

As Jane moves from place to place, the pattern of her life emerges. She is oscillating between the dangers of passion and restraint. Gateshead, her point of origin, the gate from which she issues on her journeys, is a place of physical savagery, concealed by a veneer of middle-class gentility. The indulged John Reed injures Jane. The heat of Jane's answering rage leads to further violence when she is locked in the red-room. There, rage burns out as gothic terrors reduce the child to insensibility.

Lowood is the counterpoise. The temperature is low: chill to freezing. A single fire is surrounded by rows of big girls so that the smaller are cut off from any source of warmth. The water in the basins is frozen in the mornings;

as a result, Helen is birched for not cleaning her nails. Helen. Miss Temple. Their names suggest the classics. Helen is reading a neo-classic work, *Rasselas*, a rational dialogue on the vanity of human wishes, which is conducted with serene forbearance. It is from Helen and Miss Temple that Jane learns to accept the decorums of social conduct and the virtues of humility, poverty, servitude, and self-denial. By the time she leaves Lowood eight years later, she appears a changed character: 'I had given in allegiance to duty and order . . . I appeared a disciplined and subdued character.'

Discipline is a counter to futile rage. The graces of decorum prove essential to Jane's progress through a public world. At Lowood she learns French and other subjects which will give her the means to earn her keep. In short, there are benefits at Lowood, and, in the end, it is not the pains but the gains that matter—if they can be distilled and used. Jane owes it to Lowood that she holds her own with dignity as she engages—as she must, if she is to survive—with the ephemeral norms of her age: the artifice of bloodless dolls, Adèle and Blanche; the self-absorption of vain Georgiana Reed; the mercenary snobberies of Aunt Reed and Lady Ingram, blind to the woman forming in the double-enclosure of the window seat and in the back shadows of the drawing-room. The insistently visible Blanche Ingram epitomises the taste of the age as she holds the floor with her props on show—her ringlets, her trinkets, her stock of accomplishments—while Jane, the unrecognised portent of the future, slips away. Rochester follows and commands her to remain. His refusal to let a genuine woman vanish up the stair is a gesture towards what lies beyond his time. Jane is called back—drawn into the light—for Rochester alone recognises her authenticity. To place Blanche in apparent competition is to fan Jane's love in cruel Zamorna fashion,* but it also goads her out of silence to make her famous declaration of a soul equal to his own.

Jane had left Lowood to seek 'a new servitude' but, at Thornfield, without the model of Miss Temple, she finds herself again in her

---

* Based on the Duke of Wellington who defeated Napoleon at Waterloo in 1815, the Duke of Zamorna was a character in the Brontë children's fictional saga set in the imaginary world of Gondal.

'natural element' as she awakens to needs unsubdued. It is heady to be told by Mr Rochester that she is 'not naturally austere'. A trained restraint has muffled her voice and restricted her limbs—these he will free. Yet this liberator is also the keeper of his wife. The Thornfield scenes rework the Richardsonian story of the rakish Mr B— and his high-principled servant, which Jane had heard as a child when Bessie read aloud from the pages of *Pamela* (1740). But more influential than this specific parallel is the closed-in world of Richardson's heroines: women as captives or in frantic flight, their fear of sexual injury, and their tense debates of response versus self-preservation. At Thornfield, raging fires signal passion in its erotic and destructive aspects. The fire around Rochester's bed warns of his licentious past; this is matched by Jane to the rescue. In so far as this act foretells their future, it is something of a practical answer to futile emotional abandon in *Wuthering Heights* where the dying Catherine pulls feathers from her pillow. Immured in domesticity and pregnancy, shut by her own rebellion in her room, she flings open the window as though she might fly in spirit towards the moors. The wildness of

Catherine's nature has its point of reference in Peniston Crag, the refuge of her childhood. Her need to escape the stuffy marriage to a kind but closed-off gentleman is propelled by her need to recover the nature her soulmate, Heathcliff, shares. For he, in a more distilled form than Catherine, is Nature itself: exhilarating and often anarchic. In *Wuthering Heights*, passion and society are incompatible; in *Jane Eyre*, Charlotte Brontë challenged this view, but for a long time Rochester remains a lawless character.

Thornfield exposes Jane to a thorny path—when she tries to suppress her longing for a response to her love, and later when she must face up to the perversion of passion in Rochester's past, represented by the biting animal secreted on the top floor or escaping, with malevolent intent, along the passages of the night. The most painful thorn is the alteration of a pure feeling for Mr Rochester, when she discovers his deception: 'Mr Rochester was not to me what he had been; for he was not what I had thought him.' The greatest pain is loss of trust: the loss of that direct, even abrasive truth that had provoked Jane's love.

As Thornfield presented a subtler temptation

than Gateshead to live by feeling alone, so Moor House, the home of Rivers, provides the final temptation to renounce the flesh—a subtler version of the spirit of Lowood than Mr Brocklehurst. 'There are no *good* men of the Brocklehurst species', Mary wrote from New Zealand when she received the book. But Charlotte did make a small distinction: Mr Brocklehurst is a 'black pillar'; Rivers a 'white pillar'. As missionary, Rivers does offer Jane work, a fulfilment of part of her nature—but at the cost of that vital part she had discovered at Thornfield.

In the end, the two lovers, tried by their ordeals, are reunited in their retreat at Ferndean, a place based on the ruins of Wycoller Hall, in a remotely beautiful spot, with a pebbled stream and large trees, across the moors above Haworth. This reunion could have been a bath of sentiment, but both speak with a blunt, almost brusque directness that marks their assurance: they have found a perfect mean between passion and restraint.

The last of the publishers to turn down the one-volume *Professor* was Smith, Elder, and Co.

who wrote an encouraging letter intimating that a work in three volumes would meet with careful attention. Three weeks later, on 24 August 1847, Charlotte sent them the manuscript of *Jane Eyre*. The head of the firm, George Smith, read it throughout the following Sunday, cancelling a riding engagement, bolting his dinner, and refusing to go to bed until he had finished the book. On Monday he offered Currer Bell £100 (later adding extras amounting to £500). Six weeks later, on 16 October 1847, he published it.

An explosion of praise followed. Ugly men gave themselves 'Rochester airs'. Most pleasing to Charlotte was the remark of a writer, Miss Kavanagh, that the book had been '*suggestive*' to her. This went with a report of Miss Kavanagh's character as one 'rarely found except where there has been toil to undergo, and adversity to struggle against: it will grow to perfection ... in the shade.' Reflected in Charlotte's words, she sounds like Jane. Of all contemporary writers, Charlotte most admired William Makepeace Thackeray, the author of *Vanity Fair*, who wrote at once to William Smith Williams, her first supporter at Smith, Elder:

> I wish you had not sent me *Jane Eyre*. It interested me so much that I have lost (or won if you like) a whole day in reading it at the busiest period with the printers I know wailing for copy.

Another established writer, John Gibson Lockhart (the biographer of his father-in-law, Sir Walter Scott), wrote on 29 December 1847:

> I have finished the adventures of Miss Jane Eyre, and think her far the cleverest that has been written since Austen and Edgeworth were in their prime. Worth fifty Trollopes and Martineaus rolled into one counterpane, with fifty Dickenses and Bulwers to keep them company; but rather a brazen Miss.

This 'brazen Miss' explains why the novel was regarded, for three more decades, as 'dangerous' in the words of Anne Mozley, writing in the *Christian Remembrancer* in April 1853. She complained of 'outrages on decorum' and saw 'no ... true insight into the really feminine nature. Such [as Currer Bell] cannot appreciate the hold which a daily round of simple duties and pure pleasures has on those who are content to practise and enjoy them.' Lady Herschel, visiting Mrs Smith, mother of the publisher, was shocked to see the novel in the drawing-room. Were not the Smith daughters to be guarded from its dangers? And, strangely, even Mrs Gaskell's daughter had to ask her mother's permission to read it. 'I am afraid I never told you that I did not mind your reading *Jane Eyre*', Charlotte's future biographer told Marianne, aged twenty, in 1854. Mrs Oliphant, the foremost opponent of emancipation, said that 'this furious love-making was but a wild declaration of the "Rights of Woman" in a new aspect.' She warned of 'grossness' and 'refined indelicacy'. It was often women who feared the novel, and used it as a text on which to hang warnings about a rebellious temper.

Such women particularly resented insights about desire. It is now emerging that active desire in women was taboo for reasons that were more covert and disturbing than truisms about Victorian prudery. Rochester's double standard was, of course, a norm in nineteenth-century England, and the concomitant fear was, of course, the spread of venereal disease. What is less known is that an influential body of medical and quack opinion, from the seventeenth to the early twentieth century, warned men that 'a woman was more likely to transmit such an infection the nearer she approached to orgasm herself.' This belief shaped the secret attitudes of several ages which saw women's arousal in terms of disease. This taboo may have hovered behind the double standard of reviewers of *Jane Eyre* who were anxious to determine the sex of the author: the *North British Review* which argued that 'if "Jane Eyre" be the production of a woman, she must be a woman unsexed' and *The Economist* which praised the book if written by a man, and pronounced it 'odious' if by a woman. These were the reviews most distressing to the author:

> To such critics I would say, 'To you I am neither man nor woman—I come before you as an author only. It is the sole standard by which you have a right to judge me—the sole ground on which I accept your judgment.'

In the mid-twentieth century it was common to read *Jane Eyre* as an expression of gender antagonisms, and to point to Rochester's blindness as 'emasculation'. Such readers were descendants of those first reviewers who misinterpreted Jane's longing for experience as a feminist threat. Mary Taylor wrote to Charlotte: 'You are very different from me in having no doctrine to preach.' She was surprised, she owned, to find *Jane Eyre* 'so perfect as a work of art'. This separation of doctrine and art is too rigid. Charlotte, it is true, was not a polemical feminist. At the same time, she did not abrogate ideology: she was broadening it from the arena of public rights to the more difficult, hidden, and even taboo arena of private feeling—those spaces in the mind where, as [John Stuart] Mill perceived, women were more insidiously and deeply enslaved than through more obvious restrictions to do with work, property, and the vote. This form of emancipation is yet to come; Jane portends a future we might realise. She may not be a preacher, but is something of a prophet.

The novel is prophetic in Jane's search for independence, and above all in its claim of her right to feelings of her own. She finds, in the end, the domestic union society approves, but in the process she has refused to violate her nature. *Jane Eyre* was a triumphant assertion of the inviolability of the individual soul.

CHARITY CHILDREN

JULIET BARKER

Juliet Barker was born in Yorkshire and has lived within a few miles of Haworth all her life. She was educated at Bradford Girls' Grammar School and St Anne's College, Oxford, where she obtained a doctorate in medieval history. For six years she worked at the Brontë Parsonage Museum, where she was a curator and librarian. Her biography is the result of eleven years' research in archives across the world. She is the author of several books on the Brontës and is a regular contributor to radio and television programs. She lives in the Pennines with her husband and two children.

On 4 December 1823, an advertisement for a new school appeared in the *Leeds Intelligencer*. For Patrick [Brontë] it must have seemed like the answer to prayer. 'School for Clergymen's Daughters' ran the headline. The advertisement announced that a property had been purchased at Cowan Bridge in the parish of Tunstall, one governess had already been engaged and a school would open on the premises in March or April.

> The House will be enlarged and altered for the Accommodation of Sixty Pupils: each Girl is to

> pay £14 a Year (Half in Advance) for Clothing, Lodging, Boarding, and Education: and £1 Entrance towards the Expense of Books, &c. The Education will be directed according to the Capacities of the Pupils, and the Wishes of their Friends. In all Cases, the great Object in View will be their intellectual and religious Improvement; and to give that plain and useful Education, which may best fit them to return with Respectability and Advantage to their own Homes, or to maintain themselves in the different Stations of Life to which Providence may call them. If a more liberal Education is required for any who may be sent to be educated as Teachers and Governesses, an extra Charge will probably be made.

The school was to be open to daughters of clergymen throughout the country, but it was primarily intended for those in most need and of the Evangelical persuasion.

> Donors and Subscribers will of course gain the first Attention in the Recommendation of Pupils: and every Effort will be made to confine the Benefits of the School to the *really* necessitous Clergy; and especially to those who are the most exemplary in their Life and Doctrine.

The school appeared to be tailor-made for the Brontës: they were certainly in straitened circumstances and Patrick was a committed Evangelical clergyman. At only fourteen pounds a year, the fees were half those of comparable schools, including Crofton Hall, so Patrick could afford to educate two daughters for the price of one.

A cheap education could have its drawbacks. At almost exactly the same time as the advertisement for the Clergy Daughters' School appeared in the *Leeds Intelligencer*, the same paper ran at least two horrific accounts of 'Cheap Schools'. On 6 November 1823, it reported a case in the Court of Common Pleas concerning a young men's seminary at Bowes in Yorkshire. Between 260 and 300 boys were boarded and educated there 'for the very moderate sum of twenty guineas per annum'. Apart from enduring appalling physical conditions, the boys had only two towels to share between them and, in consequence, most of them suffered from the itch, a contagious skin disease caused by a mite burrowing under the skin. Eighteen boys were particularly badly afflicted, some of them partially losing their sight and others becoming totally blind.

Another court case was reported on 22 January 1824: a schoolmaster near Richmond in Yorkshire, also charging twenty guineas a year for some eighty pupils, kept his boys in a similar state of deprivation. Up to eight pupils at a time shared a single bed, sleeping on a straw mattress, with only one sheet, two blankets (one of which covered the mattress) and a quilt in winter. Three of the bedrooms had no ceiling or under-drawing so the boys slept under the slates of the roof with buckets set out to catch the rain and snow. Virtually all of them were infested with head lice and fleas.

Any fears Patrick might have had about the Clergy Daughters' School must have vanished when he saw the list of patrons annexed to the advertisement. This was no cheap Yorkshire school of the Dotheboys Hall variety:* the list included some of the most eminent people in the land as well as a number of names well known to Patrick himself. There was Mrs Powley of

* Charlotte was at least aware of Charles Dickens' savage indictment of Yorkshire schools in *Nicholas Nickelby*, published in 1838–39; she scrawled 'Dotheboys Hall' and 'Squeers' on the back of one of her manuscripts.

Ossett, daughter of the poet William Cowper's great friend, Mary Unwin, and widow of the Reverend Matthew Powley, John Buckworth's predecessor at Dewsbury; Mrs Hannah More, the famous moralist whose exemplary works were the staple diet of female education; Joshua Fawcett of Leeds, whom Patrick had known since at least his visits to Woodhouse Grove, if not before; the Reverend Charles Simeon, the Evangelical who had been an inspiration to Patrick at Cambridge. There were even two of Patrick's own patrons on the list: William Wilberforce, who had enabled him to finish his education at St John's, and Miss Currer of Eshton Hall, who had sent him money to pay his debts when his wife had died. With the backing of such a host of the great and good, Patrick could not doubt the quality of the school. He even had personal knowledge of the founder, the Reverend William Carus Wilson, a renowned missionary preacher who had espoused the same Evangelical causes as Patrick himself and who regularly preached in the Bradford area. If Patrick had not met him in December 1822, then he would at least have had a personal recommendation of him from their mutual friend,

Theodore Dury, who was also one of the early trustees of the school. There was, therefore, no question of Patrick hastily packing off his daughters to some terrible institution simply because it was cheap and he wanted them out from under his feet at home.

The story of the young Brontës at the Clergy Daughters' School has become inextricably entwined with that of the young Jane Eyre at Lowood School. Charlotte's account of the suffering of Helen Burns and Jane at the hands of Mr Brocklehurst and Miss Scatcherd is written with such raw passion and such a burning sense of injustice that it is impossible not to identify with the girls against their persecutors. There is also no doubt that the novel was based upon Charlotte's real experiences at the Clergy Daughters' School, so it is easy to fall into the trap of believing that the fictional characters and place are accurate representations of the people at Cowan Bridge and the school itself. This is to do less than justice to both the much-maligned Carus Wilson, who is seen as the villain of the piece, and Charlotte herself, who, while protesting the truth of her account, also clearly recognised that it was not impartial. As she told Mrs Gaskell several times,

> she had not considered it necessary, in a work of fiction, to state every particular with the impartiality that might be required in a court of justice, nor to seek out motives, and make allowances for human feelings, as she might have done, if dispassionately analysing the conduct of those who had the superintendence of the institution.

Lowood is seen through the eyes of the child suffering there, not the dispassionate adult. On the other hand, the novel clearly struck a chord in those who knew the Clergy Daughters' School. Charlotte herself wrote to William Smith Williams, her editor, less than three months after the novel had been published:

> *Jane Eyre* has got down into Yorkshire; a copy has even penetrated into this neighbourhood: I saw an elderly clergyman reading it the other day, and had the satisfaction of hearing him exclaim 'Why—they have got— School, and Mr— here, I declare! and Miss— (naming the originals of Lowood, Mr Brocklehurst and Miss Temple). He had known them all: I wondered whether he would recognise

> the portraits, and was gratified to find that he did and that moreover he pronounced them faithful and just—he said too that Mr— (Brocklehurst) 'deserved the chastisement he had got'.

The unidentified clergyman was not alone in recognising the school and Charlotte later confessed

> she should not have written what she did of Lowood in *Jane Eyre*, if she had thought the place would have been so immediately identified with Cowan Bridge, although there was not a word in her account of the institution but what was true at the time when she knew it . . .

Those who did not recognise the school from the novel were left in no doubt of its identity by Mrs Gaskell, who named names and laid the blame for Charlotte's future ill health and the deaths of her sisters squarely on the institution and its founder. *The Life of Charlotte Brontë* therefore caused a furore, provoking not only legal action from Carus Wilson but also a flood of letters to the newspapers from former pupils. Their accounts, some supporting Mrs Gaskell, some emphatically contradicting her, help to build up a picture of what life was really like at the Clergy Daughters' School.

The school itself was a row of low stone cottages, built at right angles to and adjoining the main turnpike road which ran high over the fells of the Yorkshire Dales from Kendal, in the Lake District, to Leeds in the West Riding of Yorkshire. These cottages, which are still standing, were the teachers' quarters, the kitchen and dining room and some small bedrooms. At right angles to the cottages, facing the road, was an old bobbin mill which Carus Wilson had had converted into the schoolroom, with the main dormitory above. Opposite this wing of the school and backing on to the road, was a long, covered walkway where the girls could exercise in bad weather. The schoolroom, cottages and walkway formed three sides of a square; in the middle, stretching down to the river, were the small plots of garden which were tended by the pupils themselves.

Although only the cottages now remain and the hamlet of Cowan Bridge has been engulfed by a modern industrial estate, it is still possible to feel the isolation of the school's position. It stands on the lower slopes of Leck Fell, from which vantage point it looks out over an immense vista of low-lying wooded hills and lush green river valleys. In the distance lies the rough moorland terrain of the fells, rising to the mountains of the southern Lake District to the west and Ingleborough, Whernside and Penyghent to the east. There are a few scattered sheep farms, the houses built like the Cowan Bridge cottages, with stone walls several feet thick and tiny windows to withstand the excesses of the weather. When it is not hidden in low-lying cloud and mist, pulverised by torrential rain or lost in the white-out of snow blizzards, the situation is magnificent. Its dramatic beauty could not have been lost on the young Brontës.

The regime at Cowan Bridge was undoubtedly strict and austere, but this was by no means unusual at the time. Woodhouse Grove, the academy founded in 1812 to provide a free education for the sons of Methodist ministers, is especially relevant as a comparison. It was founded for similar reasons to the Clergy Daughters' School and had the same aims in mind. Patrick had a thorough working knowledge of its arrangements, having served twice as an examiner and stayed there several times during his courtship of Maria.* Unlike the Clergy Daughters' School, however, Woodhouse Grove never produced a pupil who wrote a blazing indictment of the regime in one of the most popular novels of the day. Woodhouse Grove therefore maintained its reputation as an excellent academic institution providing a charitable service to the Methodist Church. It is a typical example of the better boarding schools of the day, including places as famous as Dr Arnold's Rugby or as ancient as Oundle.

The girls at Cowan Bridge had to wear a distinctive uniform, which Charlotte undoubtedly resented because it labelled them 'charity-children'. On the other hand, they were required to be equipped with a plentiful supply of clothing: four day shifts (shirts) and three night shifts, three night caps, two pairs of stays, two flannel, one grey stuff (wool) and three white upper petticoats, two pairs of pockets, four pairs of white cotton stockings and three of black worsted, one nankeen spencer (a short jacket), four brown and two white holland pinafores, one short

* Maria Brontë, née Branwell, Charlotte's mother.

coloured dressing-gown and two pairs of shoes. In addition they had to bring gloves and a pair of pattens, which were wood and metal over-shoes for outdoor wear. Their frocks, bonnets and cloaks were provided by the school at the cost of three pounds per child. In summer they wore plain straw cottage bonnets with white frocks on Sundays and nankeen (buff-coloured cotton) frocks on other days; in winter they had purple stuff frocks and purple cloaks. The simple fact that they had to bring so many duplicate items suggests that the school was concerned about cleanliness, enabling them to have regular laundry days without depriving the girls of their clothing. This is not so ridiculous as it sounds. The boys at the 'cheap' Bowes school sometimes went four or five days without jackets or trou-sers when these were taken away to be mended, and even at Woodhouse Grove School, which was a model of its kind, the boys were only pro-vided with one suit of clothes a year.

Cowan Bridge was capable of taking up to seventy-two pupils, but when the Brontës arrived the school had only been open a few months and there was never anything like this number in their time. Maria and Elizabeth were only the seventeenth and eighteenth pupils to enter the school, and by the time Charlotte and Emily left on 1 June 1825, there were still only fifty-three pupils on the register. The ages of the pupils varied widely, the youngest on entry being six, the oldest twenty-two. Thirty of the forty-four pupils at the school when Emily came on 25 November 1824 were in the eight to fourteen bracket, including her own sisters. Emily, at nearly six and a half, was one of only three six-year-olds, who were clearly the babies of the school as there were no seven-year-olds; they appear to have been treated quite differently from the older pupils. At eight, Charlotte would have been one of the youngest and smallest girls in the mainstream of the school—an obvious disadvantage in terms of the daily scramble for food and places next to the fire. Like Jane Eyre, however, Charlotte was fortunate in finding an older girl who took her under her wing. Perhaps surprisingly, given their closeness at home, this was not either of her elder sisters, but a seventeen-year-old named Mellany Hane. She came from Bedfordshire and, with her twenty-two-year-old sister, had entered the school exactly seven weeks after Charlotte; her fees were paid by the Clergy Orphan Society. Charlotte later told her father that Mellany had frequently defended her against the encroachments of the older girls.

As was the normal practice at boarding schools, most of the girls slept two to a bed in the single dormitory which ran the length of the upper floor over the schoolroom. If *Jane Eyre* is an accurate description of life at Cowan Bridge, the girls rose before dawn, dressed by rush-light, washed each morning in basins shared between six girls (when the water in the pitchers had not frozen overnight) and went downstairs to an hour and a half of prayers before being allowed to eat breakfast. To young children straight from a loving home, where they had had a nursemaid to wait on them, this must have been a great hardship. However, it was not unusual—indeed, it was actually an improvement on common practice in many schools at this time. At one of the 'cheap' schools near Richmond in Yorkshire, there were at least three boys to one bed, and often as many as eight. Their sheets remained unchanged for two months, their under-blankets were never washed and the straw mattresses were ridden with fleas. Even at Woodhouse

Grove in 1822 there were forty-eight beds in one dormitory, twenty in another and twelve in the third. The boys had to go down into the basement to wash in three long wooden troughs filled with clean water; there was always a scramble to get there as the first boys got the cleanest water and the first use of the towels. The insistence on personal cleanliness at Cowan Bridge, which may have seemed onerous to the girls at the time, was actually prompted by a desire to safeguard their health.

The strictness of the daily regime at *Jane Eyre*'s Lowood has been called cruel in the extreme. After their dawn rising and prayers the girls had a quarter of an hour for a breakfast of porridge before lessons from nine till twelve. They then had a period of recreation and exercise in the garden before dinner. Lessons then recommenced and went on till five, when there was a short break for half a slice of bread and a small mug of coffee, followed by half an hour's recreation then study. The evening ended with a glass of water and a piece of oatcake before prayers and bed. On Sundays there was a variation in the routine. The girls had to walk two miles across the fields to their patron's church for the morning service. It was too far to return to school for a meal, so the girls had to eat a cold packed lunch in the church before enduring the afternoon service and the walk back again. Their reward was a whole—instead of the usual half—slice of bread with a scraping of butter on their return. The remainder of the evening was spent in repeating by heart the catechism and biblical texts and listening to a sermon read aloud by one of the teachers.

This fictional account seems to be rooted in fact. For the first year or so of the school's existence, the girls attended Sunday services at Tunstall Church, where Carus Wilson was vicar. The church is two miles across the fields from Cowan Bridge and still has a room over the porch which is pointed out as the place where the girls ate their food between the services. The church is even now dark and gloomy inside and bone-chillingly cold as only damp, fifteenth-century churches can be.

Remarking on the Cowan Bridge method of instilling religion into its girls, one of the Brontës' fellow pupils later wrote:

> I trust I have ever been a firm advocate for making religion the groundwork of all education but the hours devoted to sermons, lectures scripture lessons &c &c were so unreasonably *long* at Cowan Bridge, that I feel they were calculated to hinder not promote the salvation of immortal souls.

Certainly the young Jane Eyre seems to have spent more time thinking about her frozen limbs and her empty stomach than in learning the lessons of the Scriptures. Another Cowan Bridge pupil, who later died of consumption, was a more apt pupil and turned the religious tables on her teachers:

> It was usual for each pupil to repeat on Sunday morning a text of her own choice; and one who had, I believe, been punished for stealing bread, repeated in her turn, the verse which declares that men do not despise a thief who steals bread to satisfy his hunger.

Again, however, the regime at Cowan Bridge was no worse, and in some respects more lenient, than in other comparable schools. At Woodhouse Grove—and this in the days of John

Fennell's headmastership—the boys rose daily at six, had a public prayer meeting from six-thirty to seven, then spent an hour in school at reading and exercises. This was followed by family prayer and breakfast, after which lessons began at nine and continued till twelve, or half past if music lessons were on the child's syllabus. An hour was then given over to dinner and exercise, followed by lessons from one-thirty to four-thirty. The next hour and a half was spent in preaching and reading, followed by two hours, from six till eight, of public prayer, ending with supper and family prayer before bed. At Woodhouse Grove there was a chapel on site, converted from the stables of the old house, so there was no long walk to worship on a Sunday. Instead, the boys spent virtually all day at their bibles. Private prayer, reading the Scriptures and preaching replaced their usual lessons and were simply added to the normal daily diet of prayer meetings.

Nor was the discipline at the Clergy Daughters' School out of the ordinary. In Jane Eyre's Lowood, the punishments range from wearing badges for being untidy to beatings in front of the whole school. Seen through the eyes of the passionate Jane, these are terrible injustices and unwarranted cruelty, especially when inflicted on the gentle and patient Helen Burns. Once more, we find that these were standard practices in even the best schools. At Woodhouse Grove, one early governor would beat offenders on the bare flesh with a birch rod in front of the assembled pupils, having first ensured that he could not run away by 'horsing' him, putting him on the back of one of the biggest boys who held him firmly by the hands. Another, slightly later, governor would indiscriminately cane twenty or thirty boys every Monday, without enquiring if they were guilty of any misdemeanour. Delinquents were forced to wear boards on their backs for several days at a time, which were printed in large letters with legends such as 'Guilty of lying' or 'Guilty of going out of bounds'. Even at Crofton Hall, the select academy for young ladies, offences as minor as impertinence or accidental breakages were punished with the public labelling of offenders and whipping.

More than anything else, however, it was the account of the food in *Jane Eyre* and subsequently in *The Life of Charlotte Brontë* which roused most passion, largely because Mrs

Gaskell blamed it for Charlotte's 'stunted' growth and ill health which eventually killed her sisters. In *Jane Eyre*, the housekeeper was 'a woman after Mr Brocklehurst's own heart, made up of equal parts of whalebone and iron'. The breakfast porridge was regularly served up so burnt that it was inedible and dinner, 'redolent of rancid fat', was a mess of 'indifferent potatoes and strange shreds of rusty meat, mixed and cooked together'. Unable to eat these disgusting main meals, the girls became so weak that half the school fell victim to a fever.

This account seems to reflect the genuine state of affairs. Charlotte herself told Mrs Gaskell that the food at Cowan Bridge was 'spoilt by the dirty carelessness of the cook, so that she and her sisters disliked their meals exceedingly'. She was so hungry, she said, that she would have been thankful for even a piece of bread, though unlike some of her contemporaries, Charlotte did not resort to stealing. Another pupil and her sister, Elizabeth and Maria Gauntlett, who came from the south of England, were unable to stomach the north-country diet of oatmeal porridge and therefore went without breakfast for six months. When forced to eat it on one occasion, Elizabeth vomited—and was promptly dosed with an emetic. The dinner Maria Gauntlett described as 'sufficient, but not good'.

> Three days in the week it consisted of what the girls called Hot-pot or potatoe pie—pieces of meat, fat &c cut up & baked or boild with potatoes—the only vegetable ever seen—on two days there was salt beef, often ill-cured, on the other two days, fresh beef or veal—rarely if ever, mutton.

The Carus Wilson lobby, led by Miss Andrews, a teacher who had also temporarily been superintendent of the school during the Brontë period, denied there had ever been a scarcity of food. 'The daily dinner consisted of meat, vegetables, and pudding, in abundance; the children were permitted and expected to ask for whatever they desired, and they were never limited.'* As

* Miss Andrews was temporary superintendent at the opening of the school until the appointment of Miss A. Evans. Charlotte's husband Arthur Bell Nicholls and Mrs Gaskell identified her as the 'Miss Scatcherd' of *Jane Eyre*. She apparently did not recognise herself in the book, but her son did, and was furious. The sympathetic 'Miss Temple' in the novel was in real life Miss Evans, who left the school in 1826 to marry a clergyman, and died just before the publication of Mrs Gaskell's *The Life of Charlotte Brontë*.

Charlotte's husband and staunch defender pointed out, however,

> what about the *cooking* that spoiled these provisions; boiled the puddings in unclean water; compounded the Saturday's nauseous mess from the fragments accumulated in a dirty larder during the week; and too often sent up the porridge, not merely burnt, but with offensive fragments of other substances discoverable in it!

Yet another Cowan Bridge girl of the Brontë period sent a horrific account to substantiate the accusations, pointing out that

> on first reading *Jane Eyre* several years ago I recognised immediately the picture there drawn and was far from considering it in any way exaggerated, in fact I thought at the time, and still think, the matter rather understated than otherwise.

She then went on to say:

> The housekeeper was very dirty with the cooking and very unkind to the girls generally. I have frequently seen grease swim[m]ing on the milk and water we had for breakfast, in consequence of its having been boiled in a greasy copper and I perfectly

> remember having once been sent for a cup of tea for a teacher who was ill in bed, and no teaspoon being at hand the housekeeper stirred the tea with her finger she being engaged in cutting raw meat at the time. If space would allow I could give you scores of such instances as these which fell under my own observation and which after nearly twenty five years have elapsed dwell unpleasantly in my memory. Our food was almost always badly cooked, and besides that we certainly had not enough of it whatever may be said to the contrary.

Charlotte herself had seen the doctor, who was soon to become Carus Wilson's brother-in-law, actually spit out a portion of food he had tasted. Even Miss Andrews had to confess that when the doctor was called in during the spring of 1825 to attend the girls smitten with 'low fever', he had spoken 'rather scornfully' of a baked rice pudding. Her protest that 'as the ingredients of this dish were chiefly rice, sugar, and milk, its effects could hardly have been so serious as have been affirmed' suggests that the teachers may not have been sympathetic to the girls' complaints about the food.

If the skimmed milk used at the school

was sour, it would have been difficult to detect until tasted, because it does not curdle or smell bad. There was no excuse for the dirty cooking utensils, however, or the slovenliness of the housekeeper. Unfortunately, Cowan Bridge does not appear to have been an isolated case; complaints about the food at Woodhouse Grove have a familiar ring about them. As late as the 1850s, one schoolboy complained:

> Breakfast consisted of a thick slice of dry bread and about half a pint of skimmed milk, occasionally sour, and sometimes slightly warmed in winter. At dinner we generally had two courses; and supper, at six o'clock, was an exact repetition of breakfast . . . my stomach rebels at this moment at the thought of the rice, it was either boiled very dry (into 'snowballs') and then anointed with a thin unguent composed of treacle and warm water, or else baked in huge black tins, in which it looked as it if had been 'trodden under foot of men'. You had to eat it all up, or Mrs Farrar would probably give you a box on the ear, and stand over you till you did. I have many a time gone away from the table with food in my handkerchief to throw

> away, because, had I been forced to eat it, I should have been ill.*

As everyone, including Charlotte and Mrs Gaskell, was careful to point out, the filthy cook at Cowan Bridge was evenutally dismissed and replaced by a clean and efficient woman, who produced a marked improvement in the food.

The school register supports Mrs Gaskell's claim that ill health was commonplace among the girls during the early years of the school, resulting in many being sent home. Of the fifty-three pupils there at the same time as the Brontës, one died at Cowan Bridge and eleven left school in ill health; six of them died soon after reaching home. There clearly was a particular problem in the first nine months of 1825, when twenty girls (including the four Brontës) were withdrawn from the school, nine of them in ill health. Carus Wilson therefore lost more than a third of his pupils in only the second year

---

* Slugg, J.T., *Woodhouse Grove School: Memorials and Reminiscences*, London, 1885. This was still better than the Bowes school, where the boys had meat three times a week, with cakes made of water, meal and potatoes the other days: for tea on Sunday they got 'the skimming of the pot', which was usually full of maggots.

of the Clergy Daughters' School's existence. Nor did the general state of health even start to improve until 1832—the year the school relocated to Casterton—by which time another two, if not three, girls had actually died at Cowan Bridge and a further fifteen had left school in ill health, six of them to die. Though it may seem horrendous today that any child should die of fever at school, in defence of Cowan Bridge it should be noted that epidemics and consequent fatalities were an unfortunate but ordinary fact of nineteenth-century boarding school life. Woodhouse Grove lost eleven boys in a period of about ten years and there were similarly fatal epidemics at Rugby, Rossall and other public schools of the day.

All in all, therefore, the Brontës were unfortunate to be at the Clergy Daughters' School during its difficult early years. On the other hand, even then the school was no worse than many of its renowned and much-praised contemporaries and in certain instances it was actually better. Apart from the significant problem of the dirty housekeeper, there was an insistence on personal cleanliness, neatness and discipline which was not only necessary for the smooth and healthy running of the school but also inculcated the sort of personal habits that would commend themselves to the Brontës in later years. There is no doubt that Charlotte endured great hardship there: her fastidious nature was revolted by the unavoidable evils of communal school life, she rebelled against the loss of freedom and she resented the feeling that she was a 'charity child'. What she could not forgive, however, was the fact that her two older sisters died as a direct result, as she saw it, of their own experience at the school.

Maria and Elizabeth Brontë arrived at the Clergy Daughters' School on 21 July 1824. They should have gone earlier, but because they were still delicate from having had whooping cough and measles in the spring, their entry was delayed. Patrick himself escorted his daughters the forty-five miles from Haworth to Cowan Bridge; they travelled by the daily coach from Leeds, which conveniently stopped at Keighley. He stayed overnight and dined at the same table as his children so that he was able to see for himself how the school was run; he was evidently satisfied as he returned home without comment. Had there been the slightest hint of anything unusual or wrong he would undoubtedly have complained, as he was not the sort of person to allow such things to pass.

The girls were assessed by the superintendent, Miss Andrews, and their details entered into the school register. It was noted, for instance, that both were being paid for by Patrick himself, not by one of the charitable societies or by their godmothers. They had both been vaccinated and Maria had also had chicken pox. Their 'Acquirements on Entering' seem unimpressive. (It should be explained that 'ciphering' meant arithmetic, 'working' meant plain sewing and 'accomplishments' meant French, music and drawing.) Against Maria, aged ten, it was recorded:

> Reads tolerably—Writes pretty well—Ciphers a little—Works very badly—Knows a little of Grammar, very little of Geography & History. Has made some progress in reading French but knows nothing of the language grammatically.

Elizabeth, aged nine, fared even worse: 'Reads little—Writes pretty well—Ciphers none—Works very badly. Knows nothing of Grammar, Geography, History or Accomplishments'. The apparently damning reports, which are often cited as evidence of Patrick's failure to educate his daughters, are actually almost identical to every other entry in the register, regardless of age or background. There was obviously a motive to understate achievements on entry so that the school could take the credit for greater improvements. Many girls, even some of the oldest entrants who were in their late teens, did no better than the Brontës: Maria was exceptional in being able to read French at the age of ten, even if she could not parse it.

It is interesting to note that Patrick had a clear notion of his daughters' capabilities and future prospects. Maria, 'a girl of fine imagination and extraordinary talents', as even the teacher who is supposed to have persecuted her readily admitted, was to be educated for a governess. She therefore received lessons in French and drawing, for which Patrick had to pay an extra three pounds a year. Elizabeth, who possessed 'sound common sense' but was not as intellectual as her sisters, was clearly earmarked by Patrick to be the family housekeeper; she was the only one of his daughters not to be instructed in the 'accomplishments'.

Life at the school at this time was probably not unpleasant. Both Maria and Elizabeth were used to being away from home, having already experienced the rigours of boarding school at Crofton Hall. There were only sixteen other girls there to begin with and, of these, at least two were already acquaintances, if not actual friends. Margaret Plummer, who had been at the school since 21 February, was the fourteen-year-old daughter of the Reverend Thomas Plummer, headmaster of the Free Grammar School at Keighley, who sometimes officiated for Patrick. She must have become a friend, as Maria gave her a needlecase she had made herself, suitably inscribed. Ten-year-old Harriet Jenkins, who had been there since 4 March, was the daughter of the Reverend David Jenkins, Patrick's fellow curate at Dewsbury, who had undertaken duty for him so often at Hartshead.

On 10 August, just under three weeks after their own arrival, Maria and Elizabeth had a welcome visit from their father when he brought Charlotte, who was now well enough to join her sisters at the school. Patrick again stayed the night and dined with his daughters. At the end of September there was another visitor, Elizabeth

Firth, now Mrs James Clarke Franks, who was on her wedding tour; she gave each of the girls 2/6d. before leaving.*

For Charlotte, the change in her circumstances was traumatic. It was the first time she had ever been away from home and she had no prospect of returning there for nearly a year: the only holidays were the customary five weeks in the summer. She could not even keep in regular contact with her father and the younger members of the family because letter writing was confined to once a quarter. Even though her elder sisters were there it must have seemed like a perpetual banishment from the home and the family which meant so much to her. Her own entry in the school register noted that she had been vaccinated and that she had had whooping cough. Her acquirements on entering were listed as: 'Reads tolerably—Writes indifferently—Ciphers a little and works neatly. Knows nothing of Grammar,

* As Elizabeth Firth, Mrs James Franks had befriended Mrs Maria Brontë when she accompanied her husband, Rev. Patrick Brontë, to the parish of Thornton, in Bradford, where he had been appointed perpetual curate in 1815.

Geography, History or Accomplishments'. To this was added an unusual and perceptive note: 'Altogether clever of her age but knows nothing systematically'. Like her eldest sister, she was entered for the higher level of education which would train her to be a governess.

Despite her own later recollection of herself as having a very quiet career, being 'plodding and industrious', and 'very grave', the entrance register assessment is backed up by Miss Andrews, who described her as

> a very bright, clever, and happy little girl, a general favorite; to the best of my recollection she was never under disgrace, however slight; punishment she certainly did *not* experience while she was at Cowan Bridge.

. . . On 25 November 1824 Patrick took Emily to Cowan Bridge to join her sisters. For the third time in five months, he had the opportunity to observe the running of the school and to see how his daughters were faring. Maria may, by this stage, have had a slight cough but then his children were always susceptible to colds and coughs. None of them can have been so unhappy that they complained to their father as he would not have left without making some reference to this to the superintendent. He returned home unaware of the tragedy that was brewing.

The six-year-old Emily, 'a darling child' and 'little petted Em', as Miss Evans, the new superintendent of the school, called her, was an immediate favourite. Even her entry in the admissions register reflected her position as 'quite the pet nursling of the school'. It simply said 'Reads very prettily & Works a little'. Though it was obvious she did not have the other acquirements, she nevertheless escaped the usual damning litany 'Knows nothing of Grammar, Geography or History and nothing of Accomplishments'. Like all three of her sisters she had had whooping cough, but there is no record of her having been vaccinated; this may simply have been an omission on the part of the school, as Patrick is unlikely to have had some and not all of his children vaccinated. Like Maria and Charlotte, she was to be educated as a governess and Patrick paid the extra fees necessary.

As the weather grew colder with the approach of winter, the hardships of the pupils intensified. Wearing only pattens over their thin shoes, instead of changing into boots, they regularly suffered wet feet, particularly in the trail across the fields to and from church each Sunday. Charlotte, in the voice of Jane Eyre, described the 'torture of thrusting the swelled, raw and stiff toes into my shoes' and another pupil at the school ascribed her own, near fatal illness at Cowan Bridge to having had to sit in church all Sunday with wet feet. In December, Maria began to show signs of being consumptive, but her father was not informed. This was not an isolated case. The former pupil who complained of her wet feet later wrote:

> I suffered so severely from the treatment that I was never in the schoolroom the last three months I was there until about a week before I left and was considered to be far gone in a consumption. My Mother (whose only child I was) was never informed of my illness and I might certainly have died there without her being informed of it had not a severe illness of her own caused her hastily to summon me home. She was so much shocked at my appearance that she refused to allow me to return although pressed to do so. I was some time before my constitution recovered the blow it then received.

Charlotte herself suggested that her own sister, Maria, was the original Helen Burns in *Jane Eyre*. She later told her editor, William Smith Williams:

> You are right in having faith in the reality of Helen Burns's character: she was real enough: I have exaggerated nothing there: I abstained from recording much that I remember respecting her, lest the narrative should sound incredible. Knowing this, I could not but smile at the quiet, self-complacent dogmatism with which one of the journals lays it down that 'such creatures as Helen Burns are very beautiful but very untrue'.

If Helen Burns was a literal portrait of Maria Brontë, Charlotte's eldest sister was truly a model of fortitude. Patient and long-suffering in her illness, Helen bore the casual cruelties inflicted on her by Miss Scatcherd in a spirit of martyrdom. When Miss Scatcherd made her wear the 'slattern' or 'untidy' badge or whipped her for not having clean fingernails, she refused to see this as persecution, admitting that she was indeed careless, untidy and forgetful. Her punishment was therefore just and it was her duty to suffer the consequences of her misdemeanours; 'it is weak and silly to say you *cannot bear* what it is your fate to be required to bear', Helen told the rebellious Jane Eyre.

One genuine incident which occurred between Maria Brontë and Miss Andrews seems typical of the sort of treatment the fictional teacher meted out to her pupil, though it did not appear in *Jane Eyre*. There was a day when Maria was so ill that the doctor had applied a blister to her side.* In great pain and feeling very ill, she wished to remain in bed but, fearing Miss Andrews' wrath, had got up and slowly begun to dress. Before she could do so, Miss Andrews had pounced on her, pulled her into the centre of the room, regardless of her blistered side, and loudly abused her for her dirty and untidy habits. Begging some of the more indignant girls to keep calm, Maria had slowly continued to dress, gone downstairs and was then punished for being late. Mrs Gaskell's unnamed informant, who had witnessed the whole scene, 'spoke

* A 'blister' was an application which literally brought the skin out in blisters; it was intended to draw internal poisons to the body surface and was widely used in cases of consumption.

as if she saw it yet, and her whole face flashed out undying indignation'.

It seems unfortunate, to say the least, that Miss Evans did not put a stop to Miss Andrews' persecutions. The superintendent was highly thought of by all the girls at the school, including Charlotte, but 'she had her energies severely tasked and I believe did not at all times know the manner in which we were treated'. Nor did the Reverend William Carus Wilson intervene, though later pupils expressed gratitude for the personal interest and concern he showed over their state of health.

Perhaps this was just as well, for his form of religion might have distressed the dying child. Like her father, Carus Wilson was an Evangelical. Unlike Patrick, he was also a Calvinist and believed in predestination: that only a small band of 'the elect' had been chosen by God for salvation and that, even before they were born, most men were condemned to eternal damnation. Such a doctrine left no place for the individual to earn a place in heaven through genuine piety, repentance or the performance of good works. The emphasis of his religion was on sin and the certainty of punishment, not on conversion or the hope of salvation. Nor did he feel any necessity to soften or lighten this message for the children in his care.

... Fortunately for her, Maria was spared Carus Wilson's deathbed ministrations. By the middle of February 1825, it was obvious that she was seriously ill. Patrick was at last informed of his daughter's condition. He came immediately to Cowan Bridge and, when he saw the state of his eldest daughter, he took her straight back home. The distress and confusion which Maria's sudden removal from the school must have caused her sisters was compounded by the fact that they were never to see her again. For just over eleven weeks she lingered on in the final stages of consumption, nursed, as her mother had been nursed such a short time before, by Patrick and Aunt Branwell. Comforted by her father's more benevolent faith, 'She exhibited during her illness many symptoms of a heart under divine influence.'* On Friday, 6 May 1825, Maria died. She was eleven years old. Six

* This quotation from a letter by Patrick Brontë, Charlotte's father, is recorded in the margin of the Admissions Register no. 17 of the Clergy Daughters' School, Cowan Bridge.

days later, appropriately enough on Ascension Day, she was buried in the vault under Haworth Church, next to her mother. William Morgan again came to officiate, burying the child he had baptised eleven years before. Patrick, Aunt Branwell, Branwell and Anne were able to make their last farewells and attend the funeral but Elizabeth, Charlotte and Emily, still at school, were denied the comfort of observing these last ceremonies.

While Patrick was nursing one dying child, he was presumably unaware that Elizabeth, too, was sickening. Her own fatal symptoms may have been masked by the general outbreak of 'low fever', a sort of typhus probably caused by the insanitary conditions and practices in the kitchen. So many girls went down with it that the doctor was called in. He recommended the removal of the girls from the seat of infection and all those who were fit enough for the journey were sent to Silverdale, a pleasant sandy cove on the Lancashire coast near Morecambe, where Carus Wilson had a holiday house. Among those too ill to benefit from the sea air was Elizabeth Brontë. On 31 May, the day her sisters, Charlotte and Emily, travelled with the other girls to Silverdale, Elizabeth was quietly put in the charge of a confidential servant, Mrs Hardacre, and sent home. They travelled by public coach to Keighley and then by private gig to Haworth. For the second time in just over three months, Charlotte and Emily could only watch helplessly as a beloved elder sister was taken away from them.

Patrick probably had no forewarning that Elizabeth was returning home, for he would undoubtedly have insisted on his younger daughters being sent home with her. One can only guess at his feelings when a second daughter was brought home to die. Seeing the signs of consumption on Elizabeth's face, his thoughts immediately flew to his remaining daughters still at the school. Perhaps they, too, were in danger. The very next day he went straight to Silverdale and removed both Charlotte and Emily from the school. They were never to go back. Their joy at escaping from the hardships of the Clergy Daughters' School and returning to their beloved home would be tempered by the knowledge that it was a home without Maria and soon to be without Elizabeth. All Carus Wilson's dire predictions and stories of the deaths of small children must have sprung to mind as they watched Elizabeth die. Perhaps fortunately for them all, the process was not prolonged. She was already far gone in consumption and on Tuesday, 15 June 1825, at the age of ten, she followed her sister to an early grave. William Morgan returned yet again to Haworth on 18 June to perform the melancholy task of burying the third member of his friend's family.

The deaths of Maria and Elizabeth had a traumatic effect on the remaining children. It was not simply that they lost two of their sisters, but that they lost their two *eldest* sisters. The younger children had naturally looked to them for the leadership and support which elder children provide. In their case this role had taken on even greater importance because Maria, and to a lesser extent Elizabeth, had helped to fill the void caused by their mother's death so early in their lives. Once again they had been deprived of the maternal figure in the family.

The profound nature of their loss was to be reflected in all their later work. Motherless children and orphans were a feature not only of their juvenile writings but also of their novels. All Charlotte's heroines, from Frances Henri in her first novel, *The Professor*, to the schoolgirl in *Emma*, her last, unfinished work, were orphans. The absence of maternal love is a major factor in determining not only their future prospects but also their sense of loneliness and deprivation. In *Shirley*, this was of particular significance as the discovery of her long-lost mother is the crucial factor in Caroline's recovery from an apparently hopeless illness. 'My own mamma,' Caroline says, 'who belongs to me, and to whom I belong! I am a rich girl now: I have something I can love well, and not be afraid of loving.'

In *Wuthering Heights*, Emily too seems to have created an orphan world. Virtually every child, including Heathcliff, Catherine and Hindley in the first generation and Linton, the young Catherine and Hareton in the second, loses at least one parent, usually the mother. Though the effect is less crucial on the development of her characters than in Charlotte's novels, the motherless state of so many of them must be significant. The relationship between the two cousins, Linton and Catherine, particularly, is essentially that of a mother surrogate and her child.

By contrast, Anne, the youngest child, who was also closest to her aunt, creates the most normal families. Agnes Grey has a happy home with father, mother and sister and, unlike Jane Eyre, only goes to be a governess at her own insistence. Helen Graham, the heroine of *The Tenant of Wildfell Hall*, has an ordinary home life with her uncle and aunt even though her parents are apparently dead. Her suitor, Gilbert Markham, is fatherless, but not from childhood, and enjoys a robust and normal family life with his mother, brother and sister. Anne, who was only five when Maria and Elizabeth died, seems to have been the least affected, if only because she still had older sisters to look up to in Charlotte and Emily.

Though Branwell never published a novel, the loss of his sisters made a deep and abiding impression on him. For him there was no confusion between the loss of his mother and his two eldest sisters. It was the deaths of Maria and Elizabeth that made most impact. Ten years later, writing to the editor of *Blackwood's Magazine*, Branwell described the delight he had taken in the magazine as a child and quoted from memory the following lines:

> 'Long Long long ago seems the time when we danced hand in hand with our golden haired Sister whom all that looked on loved long long long ago the day on which she died. That hour so far more dreadful than any hour that now can darken us on this earth—When She her coffin and that velvet pall descended—and descended—Slowly—slowly—into the horrid clay and we were born[e] deathlike and wishing to die out of the churchyard that < for > from that moment we thought we could never enter more.' Passages like these Sir, (and when that last was written my Sister died) Passages like these, read then and remembered now afford feelings which I repeat I cannot describe.

In a long poem he wrote about the same time, he described the death of a beloved sister and her funeral solemnities. While it is dangerous to consider the poem autobiographical, as it owed more to *Blackwood's* than to the deaths of Maria and Elizabeth, there are certain graphic and haunting lines which suggest that Branwell was drawing on actual experience. When lifted to see the dead child in her coffin, for instance,

And, to this moment, I can feel
The voiceless gasp—the sickening chill—
With which I hid my whitened face.

The funeral, too, is described in terms redolent of personal experience:

All else seems blank—the mourning march,
The proud parade of woe,
The passage 'neath the churchyard arch,
The crowd that met the show.
My place or thoughts amid the train
I strive to recollent, in vain—
I could not think or see:
I cared not whither I was borne:
And only felt that death had torn
My Caroline from me . . .
Long years have never worn away
The unnatural strangeness of that day.

But it was Charlotte who was the most vulnerable and probably the most affected. She had witnessed her sisters' sufferings at the Clergy Daughters' School and she was closest to them in age. She must have felt a bewildering sense of divine injustice in the deaths of sisters she considered so eminently superior to herself. More importantly, having always been one of the 'little ones', her sisters' deaths promoted her to the role of eldest child. It was a responsibility she was always to feel and her own sense of inadequacy as to the way she filled that role may help to explain her subsequent veneration for Maria. A later schoolfriend described how

> She used to speak of her two elder sisters, Maria and Elizabeth, who died at Cowan Bridge. I used to believe them to have been wonders of talent and kindness. She told me, early one morning, that she had just been dreaming: she had been told that she was wanted in the drawing-room, and it was Maria and Elizabeth ... she wished she had not dreamed, for it did not go on nicely; they were changed; they had forgotten what they used to care for. They were very fashionably dressed, and began criticising the room, etc.

As late as 1849, Charlotte still refused to believe that a fellow pupil at Cowan Bridge might remember her rather than her sisters:

> none of them can possibly remember me. They might remember my eldest sister, Maria; her

> prematurely developed and remarkable intellect, as well as the mildness, wisdom, and fortitude of her character, *might* have left an indelible impression on some observant mind amongst her companions. My second sister, Elizabeth, too, may perhaps be remembered, but I cannot conceive that I left a trace behind me.

It was not Charlotte, but Elizabeth, who left least impression on her contemporaries at the school. Obviously less brilliant than Maria, Charlotte or Emily, as Patrick had recognised when entering her for the lower level of education, she shared their outstanding moral fortitude. The only incident concerning her which anyone brought to mind was the way she suffered 'with exemplary patience' a cut on the head so severe that she had to spend several days and nights in the superintendent's room.

On 23 September 1825, Patrick received the final settlement of his account with the Clergy Daughters' School in a long letter of condolence from the superintendent, Miss Evans. She had been ill herself, she told him, and the school had still not recovered fully from the outbreak of typhus in the spring:

> though cast down we have not been in despair but enabled to look beyond the dark valley of the shadow of death to that glorious life and immortality which are brought to light by the Gospel. May we but be enabled to hold on and to hold out to the end and the tears which now so often dim our eyes by reason of the sorrow which saddens our hearts, shall all be wiped away then when there shall be no more death neither sorrow nor crying neither shall there be any more pain seeing the former things are passed away.

Miss Evans had no inkling of the resentment Charlotte harboured against the school, for there was no connection in her mind between Cowan Bridge and the deaths of Maria and Elizabeth. She ended her letter, 'Our circle unite in kind respects to yourself with love to dear Charlotte and little petted Em.' Patrick was to be credited with £2 14s. 2d. One year of education at the Clergy Daughters' School had cost him £80 2s. 2d., nearly half his annual income. It had also cost him two beloved daughters.

A HOLOCAUST OF A CHILDHOOD

ROSIE SCOTT

Rosie Scott has written five novels, *Glory Days, Nights with Grace, Feral City, Lives on Fire* and *Movie Dreams*, which have been shortlisted for most major awards in Australia and New Zealand, and published in the USA, UK and Germany. She has also published a collection of short stories, *Queen of Love*, and a collection of poetry, *Flesh and Blood*. Her play *Say Thank You to the Lady* won the national Bruce Mason Award and was the basis for the international award-winning film *Redheads*. Her essays and articles have been published in various periodicals in Australia, New Zealand, France and Germany as well as in anthologies in Australia and New Zealand. She lives in Sydney.

The first time I read *Jane Eyre* as a young girl, I was very disturbed by the cruelties shown to her as a child. My imagination was gripped by the powerful and unacknowledged forces which caused this extreme cruelty and their effects. The first few chapters about her childhood stayed with me, pervading the rest of the novel with their power and so I remained unsatisfied and unconvinced by the happy ending. It was as if the sheer power of Brontë's writing, and her depth of knowledge of human motivation, undermined her own moral (and novelistic) intentions.

The character of Jane Eyre herself illustrates this ambiguity. Brontë's apparent intention is to convey a feisty, independent heroine. If we are to take her many spirited actions, her own interior monologue and the plot itself as our signposts, within the constraints of the time and mindset, Jane is at one level a defiant, and finally triumphant, heroine in the best romantic tradition. In the end, however, I believe this intention is subverted by other darker forces which dominate the novel and her character. It is Jane's masochism which I remember, her quiet seething submissiveness.

It is this subversion which makes *Jane Eyre* such a powerful and disturbing novel. Jane's courage is like that of a caged bird, and she is often compared to one, especially by Rochester. For all her fluttering and attempts at defiance, there is the unmistakable sense that her spirit has been strangely corrupted by the cruelty that moulded it, that she never really leaves the cage. This can be seen clearly in comparison with Cathy in *Wuthering Heights*. In the same social and religious context, Cathy, unlike Jane, remains a genuine free spirit, still whole after her trials.

These darker forces—the power of cruelty and sadism, the meaningless torture of a small child, images of darkness, suffocation, the hopelessness and terror of a small trapped being—all present in the opening chapters—overshadow everything that follows. There is a social dimension to *Jane Eyre* which Brontë herself mentions in other writings—her exposure of Evangelist schools and doctrine, for instance—but her portrayal of this dark childhood taps into another dimension altogether. It is entering a world which has its own language and nightmare logic, a logic we understand perfectly because it is about the universal and primal fears experienced by a small child. These are to do with abandonment, loss, defencelessness, disintegration of self and the terror these states evoke. There are other more subtle and disturbing descriptions, for instance of the precocious knowledge of a child who has to deal with prolonged cruelty and cannot possibly be equipped to make sense of it.

The closest modern analogy is one that has become familiar to us in modern media tales of a particular kind of child abuse: one child is singled out, often for no apparent reason, and tortured without mercy. These are not usually cases involving passionate hate, rather a frightening indifference, a methodical process of torture which often involves the whole household. It is as if there is an aberrant and tacit understanding that normal constraints can be dispensed with. The agents of social control who might normally be expected to curtail excesses and protect a child, in Jane's case her aunt, cousins and servants, are part of the torture to the point where one has a sense of their restrained but unmistakable pleasure in it. Thus Miss Abbott says of Jane before locking her in the red-room,

> 'Besides, God will punish her; He might strike her dead in the midst of her tantrums and then where would she go? Come Bessie we will leave her: I wouldn't have her heart for anything. Say your prayers Miss Eyre, when you are by yourself, for if you don't repent, something bad might be permitted to come down the chimney and fetch you away.'

The image this conjures up is indeed a vivid one of the lack of pity of the two adults involved, if we remember that 'Miss Eyre' is a very small girl, her forehead still bleeding from a cut, thrown into a dark room and locked in there overnight, in spite of her pleas and tears.

The English attitude to children common in Brontë's time and later in the Victorian era is of course vastly different from the modern awareness of their needs and gifts. The theological justification for the mistreatment of children is demonstrated clearly by Brocklehurst who is a marvellous mouthpiece for the most sanctimonious excesses. As he says, 'Oh madam, when you put bread and cheese, instead of burnt porridge into these children's mouths, you may indeed feed their vile bodies, but you little think how you starve their immortal souls!' Original sin must be beaten out of children in one way or another for their own good, and so as he says, 'his mission' is to 'mortify in these girls the lust of the flesh . . .'

The callousness towards childen was also in evidence in their use as fodder for the mines and factories of England, a practice which occurred in Brontë's time and was justified by lowly social status. Again Brocklehurst is very strong on this; he wishes to teach his pupils their 'place' for as he says,

> 'humility is a Christian grace, and one peculiarly appropriate to the pupils of Lowood: I, therefore, direct that special care shall be bestowed on its cultivation among them. I have studied how best to mortify in them the worldy sentiment of pride . . .'

For such reasons, many children from all classes were subjected to short, ugly and brutal childhoods, and this state of affairs was tolerated by a significant section of society, especially those like Brocklehurst or mine and factory owners who could profit from it. Brontë makes this connection very clear in Brocklehurst's case, his brutality made worse by the hypocrisy underlying it. Through the power of her imagination and her writing, Brontë sees beyond these spurious social and theological justifications to the cruelty that lies at the core of them.

By drawing directly from the subconscious world of nightmare in these first few chapters, Brontë enters into a child's world of suffering and compels us as readers to do the same. It is as if she is bypassing the normal adult channels of defence and logic, and aiming straight for the emotional jugular. Her writing style, a kind of cloudy clogged narrative, illuminated every now and then by a strange flash of revelation, is ideal for this dark dream description.

The disturbance I felt as a thirteen-year-old reading *Jane Eyre* was partly to do with the unacknowledged sexuality seething away under the seemingly polite prose, a sexuality I sensed rather than analysed and which I found cruel and strange. The sexuality of a thirteen-year-old is an oddly appropriate image for the sexuality in *Jane Eyre*, inchoate, naive, unexamined and powerful as it is. There is the same mixture of fantasy and a certain callous matter of factness, of melodrama and genuine suffering. Thus one of the memorable scenes for me occurs right at the beginning of the novel when Jane is attacked by her fourteen-year-old cousin John Reed. It is almost pornographic in its businesslike sadism. Jane describes him as a person who 'bullied and punished me ... continually: every nerve I had feared him, and every morsel of flesh on my bones shrank when he came near ...'

He asks Jane to come towards him,

> ... and seating himself in an armchair he intimated that I was to approach and stand before

> him . . . Habitually obedient to John, I came up to his chair . . . I knew he would soon strike, and while dreading the blow, I mused on the disgusting and ugly appearance of him who would presently deal it.

Having hit her very hard, John Reed then requires Jane to stand by the door out of the way of the mirrors and windows, the better for him to hurl a book at her head, which he does, causing her forehead to bleed. This event is described with very strong language; the whole scene is coldly and relentlessly cruel and the point of it is clear—as a small girl Jane was bullied to the point of being 'bewildered by the terror he inspired, because I had no appeal whatever against either his menaces or his inflictions.'

With the idea of childhood sexuality and sexual abuse now commonplace, it is difficult for a modern reader to ignore the sexual dimension of a disturbed adolescent boy having total control over a young girl in this way. In the pre-Freudian world of Charlotte Brontë this dimension was not only unexamined but presumably unimaginable, consciously at least. This is not to say, however, that it was not subconsciously known by her, if we go by the underlying power of sadistic scenes like these. There is almost a relish, a strange sexual hum, a disturbing accuracy at their core, and a mixture of coldness and sadism which the rest of the novel and its romantic happy-ever-after ending does not address.

If we examine the early chapters in detail, several themes emerge clearly. One of the more disturbing is the notion of Jane's 'otherness', her evil and perverse nature. Here is Brocklehurst again:

> '. . . no single deformity points her out as a marked character. Who would think that the Evil One had already found a servant and agent in her? Yet such, I grieve to say, is the case.'

In fact, all the authority figures in her childhood are unanimous in seeing her in this way. Brontë makes it clear that this reflects a universal human tendency to demonise those we wish to persecute. Her aunt tells her, before pushing her back into the red-room,

> '. . . I abhor artifice, particularly in children; it is my duty to show you that tricks will not answer;

> you will stay here an hour longer, and it is only on condition of perfect submission and stillness that I shall liberate you then.'

In dehumanising Jane in this way they can feel absolutely justified, they can have no doubts that her evil nature not only deserves but requires constant punishment. Such is the power of her contagion that 'she must be separated from ordinary people for their own safety,' or as her aunt tells John, '. . . I told you not to go near her: she is not worthy of notice. I do not choose that either you or your sisters should associate with her.'

The child as prisoner of her childhood, in a peculiarly English refinement of physical and mental cruelty, is made to spend most of her days in solitary confinement; eating, sleeping and reading alone, uncared for, unloved, uncaressed, and isolated from the outside world. Like all prisoners she is daily made to feel her worthlessness; she is daily reminded that no justice or mercy will be shown her, and like all prisoners she must be constantly on the watch for danger. This includes attacks from John and regular severe beatings from her aunt given for reasons she cannot understand or predict. Her life is a meaningless nightmare of powerlessness and punishment, and Brontë does not spare us any detail. In this lurid world Jane never hears any message other than that she is both evil and worthless. Her only ally, Bessie, is very half-hearted in her defence, threatening to tie her down at one point and telling her,

> 'You ought to be aware, Miss, that you are under obligations to Mrs Reed: she keeps you: if she were to turn you off, you would have to go to the poorhouse ... What we tell you is for your good ...'

Childhood tribulations and the emergence of the heroine unscathed from them are a staple of romantic fiction, but it is rare for this kind of cruelty to be portrayed so relentlessly and disturbingly. We have an almost visceral sense of the damage; the blows to the child's sense of self so severe and prolonged it would seem no adult could withstand them, let alone a friendless child. Even submissiveness, which is the only defence allowed, does not save her, and any other reaction is treated with frightening savagery. It is a progression of sadistic, all-powerful father figures who wield this power over her, a power unchecked by law or morality. The brutishness of John Reed, Brocklehurst's religious hypocrisy, the coldness of St John and the more ambiguous power of the father/husband protector Rochester, all have a strong impact on Jane: some of the most disturbing events in the book occur when she is at their mercy. The dream/fantasy dimension in Brontë's writing is most apparent in the characters of Reed and Brocklehurst who have the crude, almost cartoonish, power of fantasy figures.

In fact, as Brontë is at pains to demonstrate, they each feel entirely justified in this use of power by various colluding social and religious beliefs. In John Reed's case it is class and hierarchy—and Jane is low on the scale of both.

> 'You have no business to take our books; you are a dependant, mamma says; you have no money; your father left you none; you ought to beg, and not to live here with gentlemen's children like us, and eat the same meals we do, and wear clothes at our mamma's expense.'

Brocklehurst talks of the need to punish and isolate her because she is 'evil' and a liar, and when she refuses to be St John's wife he warns her indirectly that 'the fearful, the unbelieving ... shall have their part in the lake which burneth with fire and brimstone, which is the second death.'

Even Rochester, when Jane tells him she will not be his mistress, says, '"Jane! will you hear reason?" (he stooped and approached his lips to my ear) "because, if you don't, I'll try violence."'

This misuse of power over the defenceless has its most powerful metaphor in the institution of Lowood. Run by Brocklehurst in a kind of demented parody of fatherly concern, it is presented in apocalyptic terms—ragged, starving girls fighting over food, the snow falling, cold pitiless dormitories with children crying themselves to sleep every night, and scenes of children dying.

It is only for their own good and the salvation of their souls that Brocklehurst orders their rations to be cut to the bone, that he allows them to freeze all winter and has them beaten for the slightest infraction. It is only to teach them to know their place and to be submissive to it that he parades his well-fed, well-dressed daughters before their famished eyes. It is only because he cares for Jane's soul that he sorrowfully instructs the teachers to punish and shun her.

As a wonderfully savage indictment of Christian hypocrisy, there are few peers in fiction. Brocklehurst has a similar quality of serene imperviousness to reality as Dickens' Chadband in *Bleak House* but with the added streak of sadism which Brontë portrays with such unnerving accuracy.

Such unnerving accuracy is also obvious in her portrayal of the dynamics of an institution as repressive as Lowood. The boundaries between Jane as fictive narrator and Brontë herself become much more blurred in these chapters. Lowood is very similar to the school Charlotte Brontë attended as a child, and which caused the death of both her sisters Maria and Elizabeth. Brontë attributed their deaths to ill-treatment and neglect at this school, and her descriptions are incandescently indignant twenty-three years after the events. Yet the psychological 'truth' of the way such an institution damages the inmates is presented unsentimentally. Brontë makes it clear that the excessive punishment, sadism and ill-treatment caused a callousness in the pupils. Survival became a matter of preying on the younger weaker girls, stealing their food, pushing them away from the fire and bullying them.

At Lowood, meaningless, random and relentless cruelty is the norm, just as it was in Jane's childhood. In this atmosphere any act of kindness assumes a disproportionate importance simply because it goes against the norm. Even to smile to someone in this situation takes moral courage, so when Helen smiles at Jane as she sits in disgrace on the stool, Jane is immediately comforted. She feels 'inspired' to master her 'rising hysteria'.

It is clear that Brontë's own experience at boarding school is central to this part of the book. For instance, the doomed dying saint Helen is based on her own sister Maria. It is interesting to speculate on the parallels between Jane's guilt over not visiting Helen when she was dying and needed her most—'why did I not spend these sweet days of liberty with her?'—and the feelings Brontë must have had as a child when she could not save her beloved sister Maria. There is something of the guilt of a survivor here; the scars Brontë bears from this experience are explicit in the narrative.

Helen is an interesting figure, she is a rare individual who remains inner-directed whatever the circumstances. Her intelligence, courage and moral sense are strengthened by suffering.

Brontë's attempt to reconcile Helen's suffering in terms of submission, original sin and the glorious affirmation of the afterlife, has strong Dostoevskian overtones. There are striking parallels between *Jane Eyre* and *The Brothers Karamazov* with its themes of evil, the mistreatment of children, and expiation of sin. Like Ivan's questions of Father Zossimo, Jane asks Helen: What is the point of your suffering when you are innocent; why do you submit to it when you don't deserve it; and finally, how can you believe in a God who causes such atrocious suffering to the good? What is so fascinating about this comparison is that both writers' intentions are subverted by the force of their writing. As David Magarshack writes in his introduction to his translation of *The Brothers Karamazov*, 'Father Zossima's pious platitudes are never as convincing as Ivan's "blasphemies".'

Helen's philosophy—that she is indeed a miserable sinner who must not only suffer her punishment but welcome it with resignation and forgiveness as a passport to the afterlife—is half-acknowledged by Jane when she says, 'I felt that Helen saw things by another light, I was wrong and she was right.'

Nevertheless this does not convince, nor can it compete with the sheer energy of Brontë's portrayal of evil. Just as Ivan's argument is too compelling to be refuted by Father Zossima's conventional explanation, so too is the suffering in *Jane Eyre* too heartfelt, the 'truth' of it too vivid. There is an aesthetic tension between the ideal and the reality and it is Brontë's artistic commitment to her own inner truth which tells in the end. We cannot believe Helen's doctrine because it has no weight besides the brilliance of Brontë's own creation. Life in the Reed household and at Lowood is so vividly portrayed that we can recognise not only the limitlessness of the human capacity for cruelty, but also our own potential for it.

It is within this framework that Brontë must achieve redemption and catharsis for Jane—in novelistic terms make sense of her heroine's suffering by allowing her to triumph in the end.

This second part of the novel begins when Lowood is transformed into a 'truly useful and noble institution' and Miss Temple becomes Jane's kind mentor. While the early part of the novel occupies a nightmare territory peopled with monstrous figures, the second part is more like fairyland, peopled with benign characters who are kindly disposed to Jane at every turn. It is an abrupt and complete shift in focus. Once Miss Temple leaves Jane's life, there is the kind, if rather bland, Mrs Fairfax and the sweet young pupil Adèle. Later, when Jane is wandering near death from starvation, she is rescued by two dream sisters who become her lifelong friends. Even St John is a 'good' character who does not succeed in controlling her in the end in spite of his best efforts.

It is as if there are two novels here which do not fit together—the first examines human cruelty in detail, and the second is set firmly in the romantic tradition where good will always prevail and even monsters can do no lasting harm. We recognise this immediately when Rochester begins to fall in love with Jane, when Bertha does not try to murder her or even set fire to her and when the sisters rescue her from starvation. Blanche Ingram, too, is never more than a cardboard villain and is easily vanquished as the rival to Rochester's affections. We know the formula Brontë is using; we are in familiar territory again.

Rochester's courtship, for instance, is the stuff of familiar fantasies, played out in a thousand romances. It is not exactly original, nor is the ending surprising. The haughty dark-eyed aristocrat who orders the meek governess around as if she were a pet dog in need of firm but loving discipline but who soon meets his match with her is a formula we are all very familiar with. So too are the arch conversations that develop as they gradually fall in love, and the way we readers are privy to his manipulations and are reassured that all rivals will be defeated. We are not surprised that he is tamed by her spirit and virtue, sickened as he is by all the beautiful, brilliant women he has cast aside in the demimonde where he has dwelt for so many angst-ridden years; nor when all the obstacles, gothic or otherwise, are surmounted, and her 'master' finally entreats her to marry him, 'yes Jane, poor and obscure and plain as you are'.

The element of wish fulfilment is most apparent in this courtship—Jane is finally loved, desired and rescued by the most powerful authority figure of all, allowing her to attain class, wealth, status and love in one fell swoop (with the obligatory discovery that she is wealthy and of the right class) and to live happily ever after.

Within this tradition there is another fairy-tale theme, that of the testing of the beloved. The old English tale *Patient Griselda* tells of a husband who puts his wife through many humiliations which reach their climax when he makes her prepare for his wedding to another woman, which she does cheerfully and lovingly. The husband reveals at the last minute that he was only testing her to see if she really was a good wife and tells her she has passed the test with flying colours—the 'wedding' in fact is a celebration of her 'perfect' wifeliness.

Jane too goes through humiliations and misery when she thinks Rochester is to marry Miss Ingram (later we discover that he has put Miss Ingram through her own little test and found her wanting). He asks Jane,

> 'For instance the night before I am married I am sure I shall not be able to sleep. Will you promise

> to sit up with me to bear me company? To you I can talk of my lovely one; for now you have seen her and know her.'

To which she agrees.

Jane sits through evening after evening of watching him flirt with his 'lovely one' and listening to insults from the 'aristocracy'. She too passes all these tests with flying colours. As he explains to her much later,

> 'yet for a long time, I treated you distantly, and sought your company rarely. I was an intellectual epicure and wished to prolong the gratification of making this novel and piquant acquaintance.'

Later he says,

> 'there was a curious hesitation in your manner ... you did not know what my caprice might be—whether I was going to play the master and be stern, or the friend and be benignant.'

Not only are the monsters merely cardboard in the second part of the novel, but there is also a basic change in Jane's characterisation. The healthy indignation which flared up in the small child and kept her alive has been suppressed by an almost superhuman self-control. Jane is almost never testy or witty at the expense of her enemies, or indignant. She preserves an almost magisterial calm, whatever the provocation. Her decision to travel with St John as a ministering sister rather than go through a loveless marriage with him, to risk death rather than live under Rochester's roof one more night, and her kindness to the dreadful Reeds are all presented as admirable actions, as indeed they are.

But a similar kind of subversion is taking place, because for all that Jane is not a likeable heroine, in spite of what seems to be Brontë's intention. Jane is never spontaneous: her intelligence, dignity, moral strength and kindness are indisputable, but it is as if she is going through the motions, repeating a lesson she has learnt and never experienced for herself. More importantly, as an adult she is not believable in the way she was as the small hunted child. Her character has become as flawless as a diamond and somehow as cold. There is a distinct lack of the qualities that make Jane Austen's heroines so human: humour, recklessness or plain lack of judgment. Jane's sense of judgment is so magisterial that I can't help believing that she must feel a little contemptuous of lesser beings, even though she would hide it very well.

In another example of the contradictions and subversions that finally determine her character, there are long passages in the book on Jane's eminently sensible, even radical views on marriage. She believes in independence within such a relationship, and at the end of the novel describes the strong, equal and loving marriage she and Rochester achieve. It is, however, very hard to reconcile these ideas with the events and nature of their courtship. There is a strong impression of humble, almost masochistic servitude on Jane's part. At one stage, when she knows she is in love with him, and believes he is soon to be married to someone else, she says, 'Can I help you sir? I'd give my life to serve you!'

It is difficult to imagine any of Austen's heroines saying this. Similarly, when she is ordered ('it is my particular wish; and if she resists, say I shall come and fetch her in case of contumacy') to sit in the drawing-room night after night to be insulted and ignored, and to watch Rochester flirt with his 'intended', the healthy indignation we have come to expect from the young Jane is changed to:

> Ere long, I had reason to congratulate myself on the course of wholesome discipline to which I had thus forced my feelings to submit: thanks to it, I was able to meet subsequent occurrences with a decent calm; which, had they found me unprepared, I should probably have been unequal to maintain, even externally.

This self-control is lauded by both Rochester and St John as part of their attraction towards Jane, and much is made in the novel of the destructiveness of passion, rage or extreme emotion. Bertha is a horrifying symbol of the mind-destroying qualities of passion out of control.

Adèle is another character whose freely expressed emotions are shown as negative, and worse, unEnglish: 'as she grew up, a sound English education corrected her French defects ...' Happily, she became 'docile, good-tempered and well-principled.' In a rare editorial moment, Jane approvingly notes that

> the housekeeper and her husband were both of that decent, phlegmatic order of people to whom one may at any time safely communicate a remarkable piece of news without incurring the danger of

> having one's ears pierced by some shrill ejaculation, subsequently stunned by a torrent of wordy wonderment.

This carries the unmistakable message that even ordinary astonishment is better left unexpressed.

In Brontë's famous portrayal of the mad Bertha in the attic, there is a tone of loathing and dread at the lack of control that reduced her to such a slavering mindless brute. Rochester himself makes the connection when he tells Jane, 'my wife was mad—her excesses had prematurely developed the germs of insanity.'

It is very tempting to see this extreme aversion as a projection of Brontë's fear of her own rage, the cause of which she illustrates so vividly through the events at Lowood. It is always risky, however, to make this kind of assertion, as such speculations are often misleading. The delicate balance between writers' own pathology and the fiction itself, their own emotions and the fictional characters who express them, is often too complex to unravel. There is, however, some evidence that the adult Jane Eyre is operating from some core of deeply repressed rage, the rage which she expressed as a child but has learnt to contain. In one memorable passage she says,

> If Miss Ingram had been a good and noble woman . . . I should have had one vital struggle with two tigers—jealousy and despair; then, my heart torn out and devoured, I should have admired her . . . and been quiet for the rest of my days . . .

This is a remarkable image for dealing with pain.

The boundaries between Jane Eyre and her creator, as with all great novels, are ambiguous and ambivalent. We do know that the section about Lowood at least reflects the writer's own suffering, unresolved grief and anger. I am not talking about 'realism' or some superimposition of a modern psychological concept which would be meaningless in that context, but a 'felt' truth. If the value of fiction lies in the recognition of universal human responses, the two characters—Jane as tortured child and Jane as highly controlled, perfect adult—do not make satisfying sense.

In the subtle way that most powerful fiction is mimetic, *Jane Eyre* could well be a metaphor for Brontë's own process of suffering. There is no catharsis for the 'first' novel as there is for the 'second'. The child with her pathetic doomed attempts to make sense of her holocaust of a childhood is left marooned, a ghost haunting the 'second' novel, her suffering unexplained and inexplicable, her rage forever buried.

PASSION AND WOMANHOOD

BEVERLEY RAPHAEL

Beverley Raphael is Emeritus Professor of Psychiatry and Director of the Centre for Mental Health in the New South Wales Health Department. She has had a long-term interest in women's mental health and in a range of other areas including prevention in the mental health field, trauma and loss. She has researched and studied the impact of trauma and loss on the development of children and adolescents, and has studied the social and emotional well-being of young women. Another major interest is the concept of resilience and the ways in which trauma and other stresses impact on the development and growth of the individual. She is strongly committed to women's issues and to the involvement of women at every level of society.

The story of *Jane Eyre* has held readers since the time of its publication: its passion, its reverberation with human longings, its mystery, and its fulfilment.

Jane Eyre explores many of the key themes of interest in human behaviour and many of particular interest to present day workers in the field of mental health. First, the story of Jane herself is a tale of resilience in the face of childhood trauma: researchers in the fields of developmental psychopathology and preventive psychiatry seek answers as to the nature and source of resilience, in the hope that building such strengths might protect the individual from subsequent psychological problems, particularly those that may arise in the face of adversity.

Secondly, Jane's love affair with Mr Rochester symbolises the attachment of a young woman to an older man, perhaps the absent and dead father she never knew. Her attachment is, initially at least, that of a child. It progresses from a classic triangle through the failure of Rochester and Jane's relationship, to their re-engagement after he is 'maimed and made safe', suggesting a more mature relationship, less oedipally tinged—although this, equally, may be challenged by his dependent need of her. The question of dyadic (two person) relationships between men and women is an eternal one, and how they may be sustained in the realities of life and be successfully psychologically fulfilling for both partners. This relationship is fascinating in its psychological development, its loss, and its eventual fulfilment, and what it might say of the relationships between men and women, strong men and strong women.

Then there is the 'mad woman' in the attic. The care of people with mental illness has changed dramatically in recent years, yet the stigma and difficulties remain in many instances. Where is the ill person to be cared for and by whom? Will they be safe if they are cared for in the community? The 'mad' wife represents both the realities of the time in terms of mental illness, but also the enigma of madness and the fears it evokes—of violence, strangeness and uncontrollability.

Finally, *Jane Eyre* is a story of the psychological development of Jane, the young woman, and it shows clearly how much the social prescriptions of the day impacted on the individual and her development. Yet despite these, Jane represents feminist yearnings and beginnings, no doubt those yearnings reflecting at least some longing of the author herself. For Jane is determined in her resolve; independent despite her need; believing in her value even though devalued. This work teaches us something of the psychodynamics of feminism. Yet this is also balanced by the other longings that are legitimate to women's needs—having a partner, the bearing of a child. These challenges and Brontë's interweaving of these themes to conclusion, give this work the strength that has enabled it to speak to women, and to men, since it was first published.

The nature of human resilience, particularly the resilience of children in their development, has been the subject of many studies and theoretical formulations. Jane is orphaned, has no siblings and is reared in a household where she is rejected, physically abused by the older boy, and treated with hostility by Mrs Reed, her aunt, and by this woman's daughters. There is only one caring person in this household, Bessie, the servant, who does not fully understand Jane's nature, but shows some affection and concern and provides some opportunities for attachment. It is hardly surprising that Jane is fearful when punished by being sent to the red-room. Nor is it surprising that this type of treatment impacts profoundly on her health and well-being. Many children in such circumstances become profoundly damaged, often withdrawing into inner worlds. They may become depressed, or aggressive, often with personality impairment affecting psychosocial and cognitive development, and the capacity for enduring relationships. What is surprising is Jane's standing up for herself and the integrity of her views of the legitimacy of her 'self' in the face of the denial of her rights as a child or as a person—and she does this with passion. Those working in this field speak of the traits of 'hardiness' that may make it possible to deal with challenges and stresses in resilient ways. This hardiness is composed of elements of challenge, and commitment. Jane demonstrates these personal characteristics of responding to stressor situations in terms of the challenge they constitute. She does not readily 'give in'. She determines a course of action, and makes a commitment to it: she does not 'give up'.

Temperament, the responsive nature of the infant, and later the individual, may also facilitate positive or negative outcomes. Temperament may be 'easy' and engaging, 'difficult' and irritating, or avoidant. These charcteristics are enduring patterns of response. Some individuals seem to 'easily' interact with their physical and personal environments; to engage and respond to stimuli without friction. Others are more negative towards, and avoidant of stimuli, and this affects their response to others and their world.

It is difficult to see these elements in Jane while she is still living with the Reeds, as little is revealed of her infancy and very early childhood. She does not have the protective and supportive relationships that older siblings can bring to a child who has lost parents. However, Jane does engage and interact with her world, even if this was not necessarily the behaviour expected of a small, plain and dependent girl child. While Jane's difficulties are somewhat different from those of her creator in these early years, what is clear is that Jane, as portrayed by Charlotte Brontë, has a growing intelligence in her appraisal of her life and world. For both Jane and Charlotte at this young age, there was a 'safe place' to go to—the world of books and reading which gave them insights into other lives and other worlds. Both Jane the creation and Charlotte the creator learned early that one can act—even if only through engagement in fantasy, or through identification with the worlds of others—upon one's own world, to escape, to gain power, to make the unbearable bearable. While these mechanisms of control can at times lead to confusion of the real and imagined worlds, the intelligence of both girls was probably a powerful protective factor. Jane's early resilience then, rests with her intelligence, her growing recognition of her ability to act on her world (what might be called in psychological terms, her internal focus of control), and at least some attachment to one secure and caring adult.

Jane's ejection from this limited and painful home to the cruel and demanding boarding school of Lowood would surely have challenged any child's resilience. But here, too, she begins to act on her world. There is the engagement with her friend Helen and her courage and integrity in standing up for her, and her grief at Helen's death. There is intelligence in her involvement with her schoolwork, her active achievement and learning. It is well established that such experiences of success may facilitate adaptation through the adolescent years, even for children severely traumatised in childhood, and there is the significant caring adult, her teacher Miss Temple, with whom she has an affectionate and trusting relationship. The interaction of these factors as well as the change that Jane has faced through the tragedies that afflict her school group at Lowood, and her ongoing commitment to her own 'self' and its worthwhile development, suggest the culmination of strong characterological traits and the capacity both to master stress and to engage and progress through the world. It is suggested that the similar tragedies Charlotte faced in her own school experience and with the death of her sisters shaped this segment of the novel and her depiction of Jane. It would appear that she too, although marked inevitably by the loss she experienced, nevertheless developed and believed in her 'self' and her imaginary creations, her fantasies and later her writings. Jane involved herself, as do many traumatised children, in her imaginary worlds—stimulated by the books she read but fuelled by her own passionate feelings, even as a child. Charlotte and her siblings played out such family worlds of the imagination—the beginnings of the creativity that led to the powerful novels: Charlotte's *Jane Eyre* and Emily's *Wuthering Heights*. It is suggested that Charlotte may at times have had difficulties in separating the reality and fantasy—so rich and powerful was the latter—and this too happened in Jane's experience of the red-room.

The emotional neglect of Jane's first ten years may in some ways have reflected Charlotte's experiences—the clergyman father, and the early death of her mother, when she was five years old. Some research has suggested too, that while bereaved children may be more vulnerable to subsequent problems such as depression, in some instances there is a growth of creativity instead, even creative genius. Jane's creativity is in her art; Charlotte's is in her writing.

Lowood School brings a fresh set of challenges for Jane Eyre, as did Cowan Bridge, the school for clergymen's daughters for Charlotte. It is suggested that Jane's friend Helen Burns symbolised Charlotte's older sister Maria, who died as a result of illness, possibly consumption, contracted and neglected in the harsh circumstances of this school. Clearly Jane's years at Lowood School bring further harsh treatment and rejection, although in the scandal that ensues after the death of Helen and others, and the subsequent renewal of the school, Jane finds opportunities for learning and for personal growth: she responds to the circumstances in terms of the 'challenge' they constitute.

These next six years of her schooling and two years as a teacher bring a period of relative calm for Jane. The words in which her experience is described fit closely with current understandings, derived from systematic research, of those factors which promote resilience even in young people who have suffered significant abuse and neglect in their childhood.

'I had the means of an excellent education placed within my reach; a fondness for some of my studies, and a desire to excel in all.' 'I availed myself fully of the advantages offered to me.' '... I rose to be the first girl in the first class.' Thus we see significant positive achievement, and related self-esteem, emerge from Jane's use of her natural abilities and intelligence.

Fortunately Miss Temple, the teacher who had stood up for Jane, and cleared her of the charges of being a liar malevolently levelled at her by the superintendent of Lowood School, Mr Brocklehurst, had stayed on at the school through these years of Jane's life. 'To her instruction I owed the best part of my acquirements, her friendship and society have been my continual solace; she stood me in the stead of mother, governess, and latterly companion.' Thus Miss Temple constituted the caring and involved adult figure through vital years of development—a relationship essential to maturation, trust and the further development of a strong sense of 'self'—even if that 'self' was shaped by the society of the day.

The next stage of Jane's life shifts, through her own initiative, when she takes the position of governess at Thornfield. It is here that she establishes her independence, finds herself a secure 'home' that is non-institutional, and to which she becomes attached, both to the environment and the people. Here Charlotte Brontë carefully and subtly sets the scene for Jane's lifetime relationships, particularly that with Rochester. But even before she meets him she is curious as to the 'laugh' and 'strange murmurs' which she is led to believe are from Grace Poole and so the 'mad woman' becomes subtly part of the background of life at Thornfield Hall.

Jane settles into her new life. Rochester returns and their chance meeting symbolises the beginning of their relationship. Jane has known few men and they have been her superiors. Of Rochester she says, 'he was past youth, but had not reached middle age . . . I had no fear of him, but a little shyness.' She is reassured because he is not 'handsome, heroic looking or young.' Nor is he responsive, '. . . but the frown, the roughness of the traveller, set me at my ease.' According to Jane's ruminations as she continues on her way after helping this then unknown man, she is pleased to have helped, even if transitorily, because it is 'an active thing, and I was weary of an existence all passive.' This 'masculine', 'strong, dark and stern' image of Rochester stays with Jane. It is then that we sense the first flavour of the powerful sexual attraction that is central in Jane and Rochester's relationship.

This relationship is sensitively drawn with the progressive build-up of tension between the master and his ward's governess. Rochester interacts with Jane to challenge her to respond—he is 'sir' and she is in part submissive to this dominance, in part resilient and holding on to her self. Yet she sees the possibility of a relationship between them (before it is overtly one of love) because he is not handsome, and she is plain, and because he does not demonstrate polite or gentlemanly ways toward her, which would emphasise the barrier of class. Jane is safe to relate to him, she thinks, because of the social distance, but she becomes 'engaged' in this relationship because of the safety of these distances of age and rank, and perhaps too because this is the first man who has ever interacted with her as a person. Yet the relationship develops, at Rochester's initiation, even with the acknowledged differences of age and experience. He shows his attraction to Jane's naïvety and child-like qualities—he cannot tell her age—she has no parents, she is a mystical creature. There is progressive disclosure of his life to her and of hers to him. As Jane warms to him she says, 'I felt at times as if he were my relation, rather than my master', '... so happy, so grateful did I become ... that I ceased to pine after kindred,' and these changes 'made his face the object I best liked to see.'

Jane's feelings are more passionately acknowledged after she rescues him from the attempt on his life by the 'mad woman'. He shows his gratitude and regard for her and touches her, holding her hand. She cannot sleep but is 'tossed on a buoyant but unquiet sea, where billows of troubles rolled under surges of joy.' There is alternating hope and promise, loss and threat, building the tensions in this relationship. The triangular aspect is reinforced when Rochester appears likely to wed another, yet each time there is threat, it increases his intimacy with Jane. There is power and passion in this relationship, a shadow of its sexuality. Yet although she sees them as equals in the sensitivity and interests revealed in their conversations, it is still to 'sir', her 'master', she relates.

Jane's return from visiting her dying Aunt Reed brings the recognition of her love for Rochester, even though it flies in the face of what she believes to be his inevitable marriage to another. She speaks of 'my pleasure in meeting my master again', and how, despite the belief in his impending marriage to another '. . . never had I loved him so well'. Jane's pain at the thought of separation from him, and his declaration of love and proposal of marriage, bring their relationship into the open for both—yet she accepts this proposal from 'sir'. The shock of the revelation of his existing marriage tears apart Jane's hopes, yet she forgives him in her heart and flees for fear she will succumb and become his mistress. 'Mother' appears to her in a trance-like dream advising her to flee temptations, and she obeys. Jane struggles against her powerful attachment to Rochester. The reader cannot doubt her conflict. The passionate sensuality of the naïve and 'innocent' governess is subtly depicted, yet it both shocked and drew the readers of the time, as it does today. The dark sexuality and savagery of Rochester is a strong counterfoil. Yet it is the sexual nature of the woman, Jane, that is at the core of the novel. The sexuality of women was negated in Charlotte Brontë's time, or was seen as 'mad' and 'insatiable', as Rochester characterises Bertha Mason. But it is Jane's understanding of the truth about women and men, that was intuitively recognised, identified with, and vicariously enjoyed by readers.

Jane's attachment to Rochester is very strong and survives despite the pain of their separation. Powerful attachment ideation calls her to him after a long period of suffering and adaptation with the Rivers family. She rejects a proposal from St John Rivers, her cousin, but is wavering when she hears a voice calling 'Jane, Jane, Jane'. She is now a woman of substance with her own inheritance. Rochester has been blinded and crippled by the fire that killed his 'mad' wife. They are reunited in a powerful, passionate and evocative scene: 'my dear master . . . I am come back to you.' Jane supports and cares for him and their love comes to fulfilment as she helps her maimed master to heal. This sensitive, strong and complex relationship between a man and a woman carries lasting significance: the love of the older man for the girl child who would be good for him; the idealisation by the girl of the older man—master, father, safe and unsafe, exciting, erotic, forbidden, belonging to another, but ultimately the woman's own. The other is defeated, the father is no longer master, but a partner in love. This story has held its power over many generations because of these eternally evocative tensions and the yearning for their fulfilment.

Bertha Mason, the sad and tortured woman who is portrayed as evil and dangerous, is the wife who cannot be acknowledged, but also the uncontrollable face of madness. Her care at this time cannot have reflected any of the understanding of madness that is now available. It is likely from Jane's descriptions that Bertha suffered a severe and uncontrolled psychotic illness. This depiction also raises the themes of sexuality and madness: cause or effect. Rochester implies her depravity is the cause: this is the stereotype of madness as a symbol of uncontrolled sexual desires, or uncontrolled aggression. Yet what is most threatening, is the inherent recognition of these forces in each of us, and the sometimes fragile boundaries of normality.

Bertha was hidden away, as madness has often been, and her existence was perceived as a real threat. After she wounded her brother, and threatened Rochester's life, she retaliated further, setting fire to Thornfield Hall. This led to her own death. As a character she is subtly woven through this book, with some empathy for her suffering. Jane's words reflect Charlotte Brontë's understanding of this, as she reproves Rochester: 'you speak of her with hate—with vindictive apathy. It is cruel—she cannot help being mad.' We know little of her in terms of her illness—perhaps this was a 'madness' of schizophrenia, or perhaps an organically induced psychosis. Whatever it was, she reflects the fear and stigma, dread of danger, difficulties of care, and suffering of those with a mental illness and their families both then and now. Many families whose ill members are difficult to manage, experience dread and concern about the behaviour of the sick person and this comes to terrible fulfilment for Rochester and Jane.

Jane's life as a woman is the fabric of this novel, from her girlhood to young womanhood, from her love and loss of Rochester to her fulfilment as his partner and the mother of their child. It has been suggested that the passion inherent in the novel and its powerful emotional tone shocked many at the time of its publication.

It would have been inconceivable to many that a woman, a young woman and a clergyman's daughter, could have depicted so realistically the compelling human dramas of Jane's adulthood. Jane was independent and clear in her strength and resolve—in her acceptance of Rochester as they interacted and their love blossomed, in her acknowledgement of their equal status—while still acknowledging the social mores of her time. Jane was independent, and although powerfully attached to Rochester, clear in her rejection of the situation he offered when his previous marriage was revealed. Jane was independent in her flight and retreat, knowing she might be unable to resist her love if she stayed. The torrid account of her flight, her fortuitous support by the relatives she coincidentally finds, and her inheritance are shown to reflect, but not change, her basic nature.

The portrait of Jane is of a strong and determined young woman. The resilience of her childhood shows in her endurance, commitment and determination as an adult, an adult responsive to others, but clear too in her own needs when she chooses to return to Rochester, the central pillar for her existence. That Jane reflects

Charlotte Brontë is undoubted, as is the fact that Jane is a strong woman, a woman cognisant of her own rights, ahead of her time in her ways, although still shaped by the demands of her society. For both these women, Charlotte and Jane, there is the fulfilment of marriage—sadly for Charlotte, close to the time of her death. But Jane is portrayed in a fulfilled and loving relationship, with her husband and baby son, 'living happily ever after'. As she says, '. . . I am my husband's life as fully as he is mine . . . we are perfectly suited in character—perfect concord is the result.' Brontë recreates Jane's strengths and independence in her equal partnership with Rochester—a dream for many women but a reality for few. *Jane Eyre* has held its power because these dreams and yearnings are eternal: to be strong; to be oneself; to be plain but valued and loved for oneself; to love perfectly and passionately. These are the core themes of human experience.

janeyre@windoW
OUT OF THE RED-ROOM

CARMEL BIRD

Carmel Bird's latest collection of stories is *Automatic Teller*. Her books include *The White Garden, The Bluebird Café, Dear Writer* and *Not Now Jack—I'm Writing a Novel*. Her novel *Crisis* was written under the pen-name of Jack Power. She has edited an anthology of writing about music, *Red Hot Notes*, and another anthology titled *Daughters and Fathers*. Several of Carmel's books have been published in the UK and the US.

Reader, I e-mailed her.

In her reply she said that she has been very disappointed with all the movies she has seen about her life, and that she has decided to take matters into her own hands and develop a CD-Rom. Setting aside for the time being the need for $500,000 development funds, we began a lengthy correspondence on the subject.

She sees her life as a pilgrimage, as a search for a home (indeed, for a house—she has been an intrepid house-hunter), and has, she believes, found her true place at the lighted window of the computer, using the new program Governess.

Confined as I am to these words on the pages of a book, I nevertheless wish to discuss with you some of the ideas we have come up with in our correspondence.

For many years Jane believed herself to be an orphan with no family and few prospects, until she learned, after many difficult and heart-breaking experiences, that she was in fact a woman of means. She also (after the most dramatic set-backs) married the man of her dreams, although not until after he had been severely injured and was crippled and blind.

She has always been an observer—a person who likes nothing better than sitting in a window-seat and watching the weather and the countryside—as well as a painter, writer and teacher, and woman of action. Added to that she knows so much about architecture and furnishing that she would do well to go into real estate or interior design.

'A spare parlour and bedroom I refurnished entirely, with old mahogany and crimson upholstery; I laid canvas on the passage, and carpets on the stairs.'

Take for example this piece from chapter one of her story:

> I mounted into the window-seat: gathering up my feet, I sat cross-legged, like a Turk; and, having drawn the red moreen curtain close, I was shrined in double retirement. Folds of scarlet drapery shut out my view to the right hand; to the left were the clear panes of glass, protecting but not separating me from the drear November day. At intervals, while turning over the leaves of my book, I studied the aspect of that winter afternoon.

Unable to go for a walk, she studies the world in and from the window-seat, and then she sets out on the voyage of her life, the walk that will take her from this house, Gateshead, on to Lowood School, thence to Thornfield Hall, and then to Moor House and ultimately to the manor house of Ferndean, with, as I suggested before, many a sorry detour.

I found it necessary to explain to Jane that the early scene in the window-seat comes over to any post-Freudian reader as a back-to-the-womb type deal with red moreen cervix and labia and so forth. She then pointed out to me that this womb had a nice plate-glass panel through which she could check the weather, but she conceded that it was a womb of sorts. A gesture towards the test-tube baby, perhaps. But certainly a signal to a reader, even a pre-Freudian reader, that the tale to be told, while possibly depicting the true events of the life, will have much of the quality of a dream, of a visit to an unconscious mind. I referred her to the first page of Simone de Beauvoir's *Memoirs of a Dutiful Daughter* where there is a statement: 'Our apartment was red', and then the description of the red upholstery, silk hangings, stained glass, velvet curtains. Jane was enraptured, and when it got to the knee-hole under Simone's father's desk, she said it was, in a curious way, as if she was reading about herself.

Taking our cue from Jane's window-seat, we decided to highlight every window in the text, and lo and behold the thing was—what shall I say—riddled, bejewelled—with fenestration.

Imagine then, the CD-Rom. Click on *window* in the opening paragraph and you will discover a lengthy menu of other windows you might care to know about in the story. I should say here that references such as Simone de Beauvoir and Freud and such will be marked in the text and will give access to a wealth of information when the user clicks on them.

A *window* is a wind-eye, the word coming from Old Norse 'vindauga' meaning a small hole in a wall through which air and light and images can pass. The sheet of glass you place between yourself and the outside world is a membrane which separates you from the action while giving you a framed version of the way things are. When you are outside looking in by the window, the glass is a barrier to the world within. To break a window is to violate a taboo, to rend the veil that hangs across a threshold marking the boundary between inside and out.

> Left alone, I walked to the *window*; but nothing was to be seen thence: twilight and snowflakes together thickened the air, and hid the very shrubs on the lawn. I let down the curtain and went back to the fireside.

> I went to the *window*-seat and fell to breathing on the frost-flowers with which the window was fretted, and thus clearing a space in the glass through which I might look out on the grounds,

> where all was still and petrified under the influence of a hard frost.

You see the kind of thing. And you will also have noticed that the world away from the fireside is prone to frost and ice and snow. Of course the CD-Rom can bring you coloured pictures of what Jane could see when she looked out her various windows. Hungry robins and leafless cherry trees. Photographs of the English countryside in winter. You could have clips from the movies which Jane herself holds in such low esteem.

Think how it would be, while watching a close-up, perhaps an animation, of hands being washed and taking out splendid shreds of silk and satin and making a bonnet for a doll, to hear Bessie singing the ballad in chapter three:

> My feet they are sore, and my limbs they are
> weary;
> Long is the way, and the mountains are wild;
> Soon will the twilight close moonless and dreary
> Over the path of the poor orphan child.

Once again there is dramatic contrast between the sweet softness, artifice and luxury of the indoor activity, and the chilly realities of the world outside, the world into which Jane must go if she is to make her way, make herself, realise her dreams and possibilities. The sentiments of Bessie's song are echoed in Jane's life story at the time when she has left Thornfield Hall and is in danger of wandering the roads until she dies.

It is drama that propels Jane, the poor orphan child, into the moonless twilight to begin her pilgrimage. There's the battle with John Reed and the imprisonment in the red-room, and the fit she has in that room, and her subsequent banishment to Lowood School. From the red curtained window-seat to the red curtained prison of her late uncle's death-chamber. The indoors may be womb-red, but it is also hell-red. The fires of Jane's own anger burn brightly within her so that the red of her cell mirrors her own state of mind. It is really quite unusual for a prison cell to be red, the colour adding a dreadful dimension to the cloistered room. And just as the word *window* is a tag for the CD-Rom, so is the word *red*. The text is drenched in redness—crimson, scarlet, ruby, cherry, mahogany, pink, rose. Red.

'Take her away to the *red*-room and lock her

in there.' This, surely one of the most awful sentences ever spoken, by Mrs Reed in chapter one.

What you really need here is some virtual reality so that a reader can be locked in the red-room. Take the reader away to the red-room and lock her in there.

Red is the colour which appears at the lower or least refracted end of the visible spectrum, and is familiar as the colour of blood, fire, the sun, the poppy, the rose and ripe fruits. Red is for danger; it is the colour of calamity, murder, sacrifice. It represents the king, the masculine, active principle, but also the red goddess, governor of the red events of birth and death. Sexual excitement, anger, love, health, vibrant life and dynamic emotion.

As with *window*, there is a long menu for *red*.

Mr Reed died in the red-room, nine years before Jane was put there to punish her, and the room contains his bed, like a tabernacle, its massive pillars of mahogany hung with deep red damask curtains. The bed is still furnished with white mattresses and pillows, covered with a white quilt. A white chair and footstool resemble a pale throne. The bed and chair loom and glare in the gloom of the chamber where the walls are pinkish fawn. The carpet is red, and the curtains at the two large windows are festoons and shrouds of the same deep red damask as the bed. Wardrobe, chairs and toilet table are of mahogany, solid, glowing red. This is nightmare land.

The wardrobe contains a secret drawer where Mrs Reed keeps documents, jewels and a miniature of Mr Reed. I wondered how Jane knew about this, but she said she couldn't remember. Wardrobes, an obvious spot for hiding important or shameful secrets, feature prominently in the story, but not as prominently as windows.

The bed rose before her. On her right she had the wardrobe with its subdued and broken reflections; on her left the windows with the blinds down and the terrible red curtains. Between the curtains was a great looking-glass in which she could see the 'vacant mystery of the bed and room'. Everything looked colder and darker in the mirror, and she could see her white face and arms, and her own glittering eyes of fear, the sole objects moving in the room. She resembled a ghost, a tiny phantom, half fairy, half imp, like one of the creatures in Bessie's evening stories coming from lone, ferny dells in the moors and appearing before the eyes of belated travellers.

You will notice how very particular Jane is about giving you her position in the room. She is forever doing this, and telling you about going through doorways, entering this room or that room—a bit like giving stage directions. She hears clocks and bells and thereby knows what hour it is and what this means, and what she has to do. The church bells and ticking, chiming clocks are very useful and atmospheric on the CD-Rom.

She shook her hair out of her eyes and looked away from the mirror into the room where she thought she saw a ghost, heard the rushing of wings, felt a presence, began to choke, rushed to the door and shook the lock, screamed and fell down in a fit. Then all hell really did break loose, and after her delivery from the red-room, she was, in due course, sent off to school.

There is much to explore in the red-room, but before we do that, let's look at a couple of other items from the *red* menu. The red is often associated with fire and light.

> We were, as I have said, in the dining-room: the lustre, which had been lit for dinner, filled the room with a festal breadth of light; the large fire was all red and clear; the purple curtains hung rich and ample before the lofty window and loftier arch; everything was still, save the subdued chat of Adèle (she dared not speak out loud), and, filling up each pause, the beating of winter rain against the panes.

And later, 'I crushed his hand, which was ever hunting mine, vigorously, and thrust it back to him red with the passionate pressure.' (Jane and I discussed the sad irony of this, in the light of what happened to Edward's hand later on.)

Jane saw her image in the red-room mirror, and fancied herself to be half imp and half fairy. And, as if he sees her mirror-image too, Rochester first and often characterises her in this way. Jane is out at sunset (the sun sinks crimson behind the trees), watching the rising moon and the blue smoke of the chimneys when she hears in the distance the metallic clatter of a horse with its rider. She thinks this is ominous and spooky, and then she is startled by a black and white Newfoundland dog, followed by the horse. They pass her, but then the horse slips on the ice, bringing the rider down. She goes to help him and discovers by the light of the moon that he is dark, stern with angry eyes. He goes his way and she returns to Thornfield.

> I heard only the faintest waft of wind roaming fitful among the trees round Thornfield, a mile distant; and when I glanced down in the direction of the murmur, my eye, traversing the hall-front, caught a light kindling in a window: it reminded me that I was late, and I hurried on.

When she later meets Rochester (for the traveller was he) he accuses her of being a fairy or a goblin who has bewitched his horse, and the characterisation of Jane as a sprite of some kind runs always through his thoughts and language. The ideas in her paintings, he says, are elfish. She saves him from being burnt to death in his bed, pouring water on him, and he says, 'In the name of all the elves in Christendom, is that Jane Eyre? What have you done with me, witch, sorceress?'

'Is this my pale little elf?' he says.

We plan to have a terrific lot of fun with fairies and elves and goblins on the CD-Rom. I would wish to have a huge catalogue of images from such as J.A. Fitzgerald and Richard Doyle and Ida Rentoul Outhwaite. They are so perfectly expressive of the repressed and crippled eroticism of Jane's text, which, by the way, she admits, on reflection, after a fair bit of e-mail on the subject.

You will have noticed the windows popping up, and also, probably, the moon. The moon is another word with a big menu, as you can imagine. *Moon*, satellite of earth, secondary planet, light derived from sun, reflected to earth, dispels darkness of night etc. And the moon is symbolic of cyclic time, controlling the tides, the rains, the seasons—Jane is as I said very keen on the seasons and the weather—and many events in her story take place by the light of the moon. It represents, after all, the feminine principle, and (very important) moon goddesses are weavers of destiny. Jane took off on her life journey, determined to weave her own destiny—the fact that she was actually an heiress and not really such an orphan was just a sort of bonus, I suppose. She sees it that way.

'Little things recall us to earth: the clock

struck in the hall: that sufficed; I turned from moon and stars, opened a side door, and went in.'

Jane's eyes glittered in the red-room mirror, and from beginning to end the text is alert with eyes, sights, visions, perspectives. The final optic comment is Rochester's loss of one eye, loss of sight in the other, and then his regaining, under the influence of Jane's love and concern, some sight. Their child inherits his father's eyes—large, brilliant and black. I am longing to put anatomical drawings and photographs of eyes on the CD-Rom. I have pointed out to her that one of the beauties of interactivity is that a reader can choose not to look at things she doesn't care for. Mrs Reed has 'Cairngorm' eyes, a description I find blissfully horrible.

We had a discussion about the names of the houses in the story. I asked her whether she had used the real names, or whether she had invented them. They are so apt. How, in life, could they be so apt? But she assured me they were the very names of the houses, and pointed out to me the descriptive names of many a country house in Yorkshire as evidence—Stonegappe, Greycliff. We decided to represent the houses with cartoons, animations, and walkthroughs.

Starting with Gateshead, then. In the early chapters, because she is intent on travelling far from Gateshead, closing the gates behind her, Jane's principal detailed description is of the red-room, although we know there is a porter's lodge and have the sense that the house is comfortable and reflects a certain prosperity. And later, after living at Lowood and Thornfield, when she visits the dying Mrs Reed, she speaks only of the 'hostile roof' of the exterior, concentrating on descriptions of Mrs Reed's bedroom which is amber, not red.

The image that has always dominated my memory of my first reading of the text when I was fifteen is that of the red-room, and somehow, the passion and the details of the writing there convey to me the sense, the feeling of Gateshead.

The verandahs of Lowood, the refectory, the dormitories, the classrooms, are dominated by an atmosphere of cold and grey, bare planks and stained plaster, and the school is built in a hollow, a forest-dell which is a cradle for fog and fog-bred pestilence. After Jane's companion Helen Burns has died of fever, Jane goes to the window and looks out. 'There were the two wings of the building; there was the garden, there were the skirts of Lowood; there was the hilly horizon.' Again she is looking beyond the house which is a kind of prison. It is when she gets to Thornfield where she is to be governess to Edward Rochester's ward Adèle that she describes the house as she approaches it.

'We now slowly ascended a drive, and came upon the long front of a house: candlelight gleamed from one curtained bow-window; all the rest were dark.'

She crosses a square hall with high doors all round, and then she goes into a room

> whose double illumination of fire and candle at first dazzled me, contrasting as it did with the darkness to which my eyes had been for two hours inured . . . A snug small room; a round table by a cheerful fire; an armchair high-backed and old-fashioned . . . The steps and bannisters were of oak; the staircase window was high and latticed; both it and the long gallery into which the bedroom doors opened looked as if they belonged to a church rather than a house. A very chill and vaultlike air pervaded the stairs and gallery, suggesting cheerless ideas of space

> and solitude ... I looked at ... a bronze lamp pendant from the ceiling, at a great clock whose case was of oak curiously carved, and ebon black with time and rubbing ... The hall-door, which was half of glass, stood open; I stepped over the threshold ... It [Thornfield] was three stories high, of proportions not vast, though considerable: a gentleman's manor-house, not a nobleman's seat: battlements round the top gave it a picturesque look. Its grey front stood out well from the background of a rookery, whose cawing tenants were now on the wing.

We are going to have a lot of fun on the CD-Rom with the rooks—they are like emblems of Thornfield Hall, the other face of fairies, in a way. And of course the text is marked by dualities like that. There's a lot of black and a lot of white; fire and ice; red and white; kind and cruel; good and evil; life and death; sun and moon; winter and spring and so forth. Clarity and obscurity. Mr Brocklehurst and Edward Rochester are both represented as big black phallic objects against the small white labial-winged fairy of Jane Eyre.

I talked to Jane about the coincidences between some of the people's names and their significance in the textual themes, how apt it is that Edward, the rock, the earth, is called Rochester, and she, the airy fairy one, is called Eyre. Then there's the cool spiritual goodness, saintliness really, of St John Rivers. She agreed that the coincidences were striking. She regretted that, in the scheme of things, Grace Poole should be called Grace Poole, but thought perhaps there was a deep irony there. I said it was then a pity that Bertha Mason's name didn't suggest fire, and Jane agreed. She confessed to inventing the name Brocklehurst, saying the model for the character was Rev William Carus Wilson.

Chapters twenty-five and twenty-six are very important not only to the narrative but to the structure and texture, the unconscious content of the novel. Two key dreams are in there, and *dream* has a menu on the CD-Rom. I suggested to Jane that from the moment she fell into the fit in the red-room, the whole thing could have been a dream, with dreams and nightmares within dreams. She agreed with this, but laughed (e-mail laughing is <:—)>) and said she wished that half of it *had* been a dream. Like Alice. But although Jane enjoys the story of Alice up to a point, she says she finds much of it sickeningly erotic. I backed off when she said that—I had at the time been about to embark on some remarks about the castration imagery of Edward's crippled hand, and the impotence of his blindness. Better not say.

The word *dream* is quite interesting. There was a Middle English word 'dream' which meant mirth, joy and music, and nobody seems to know what relation this word bears to *dream* as we know it. Our *dream* is related to Old Frisian (dram), Old Saxon (drom) and Old High German (troum) and signifies a train of thoughts and images passing through the mind during sleep. Jane's story was published in 1847 and Freud didn't publish *The Interpretation of Dreams* until the beginning of the twentieth century, and it's worth noting that the six hundred copies of the first edition of the latter took eight years to sell. This was probably because a frank discussion of dreams was very unfashionable. Jane of course didn't talk *about* dreams, but recounted the events that came to her in dreams without much comment or any analysis.

She has seen Edward's face 'all kindled, and his full falcon-eye flashing, and tenderness and passion in every lineament.' She has left her wedding dress in the wardrobe, addressing it as 'white dream', and she has walked in the orchard under a blood-red moon. Her eyes are glittering strangely and she describes Edward as 'most phantom-like'. She tells him the stories of her two dreams.

It's best if you read the whole thing in chapter twenty-five; you'll be able to imagine how exciting the dream content of the CD-Rom will be. Imagine the sequences if they were done by Fellini.

Dream one: She is following the windings of an unknown road, carrying a child, conscious that Rochester is in the distance somewhere, getting further and further away from her.

Dream two: She sees Thornfield Hall as a ruin, the retreat of bats and owls. It's a cold and moonlit night and Jane stumbles along carrying the unknown child, who clings to her neck in terror. She sees Edward disappearing on his horse, stands on a thin wall which crumbles, and the child rolls away from her.

Jane woke from that dream to find a terrible apparition in her room, a large woman with thick dark hair, wearing a straight white dress which resembled a shroud. This woman took

Jane's wedding veil from the wardrobe, put it on, and looked at herself in the glass. Jane saw the fearful, ghastly face in the mirror. 'It was a discoloured face—it was a savage face. I wish I could forget the roll of the red eyes and the fearful blackened inflation of the lineaments.'

This was of course sensitive material for me to discuss with Jane, but she is very resilient, and we were able to go over it in detail. She said the woman resembled a vampire, and agreed that it would be interesting and OK to use some clips from various vampire movies to illustrate the point. I said that most of these were pretty crude and unconvincing, but she said she still thought it was worthwhile. What she saw in her bedroom was much, much more frightening than anything she has seen on the screen. What you'd need to get, she said, was not virtual reality, but virtual dreaming, even though the woman in her room was *not* a dream. The woman tore the veil in two. 'The veil of the temple,' I said. 'Pretty symbolic.' And Jane agreed.

Edward told her it was Grace Poole, and then after the wedding was aborted by Richard Mason, she discovered that Edward had lied, and that the hideous woman in her room was in fact Bertha Mason, Edward's mad wife. The way Jane described her she sounded like the embodiment of unconscious, buried rage, and yet she had been real.

Jane then told me about something that still makes her blush with shame and embarrassment. When *Jane Eyre* went into its second edition, it carried a dedication to Thackeray. It wasn't until after the edition was printed Jane learned that Thackeray's wife was, like Bertha Mason, insane.

Perhaps the most intriguing and significant point in Jane's story is reached in chapter thirty-five where she asks heaven to show her the right path (ever the pilgrim). This is a supernatural and/or psychological event, having something of the nature of dream, but all the more powerful because it does not take place during sleep. Is it the will of heaven that Jane should marry St John Rivers? The candle is dying out, the moon is filling the room, and Jane's heart is throbbing.

But her heart is stopped by a thrill of inexpressible feeling, not unlike an electric shock (advanced talk, I thought, for 1847). 'Eye and ear waited while flesh quivered on my bones.' And what she hears is the voice of Rochester calling her name. She calls out in obedience and goes rushing into the night, and returns filled with resolve. She will not marry St John, but will set out in search of Rochester.

I told her I had always breathed a sigh of relief at that point because the thought of her going off as a missionary like Deborah Kerr or Audrey Hepburn characters was too ghastly. What about her love of ruby glass and oriental carpets and feather beds and oak and mahogany and looking-glasses and flowers and enormous fires? I hesitated when I said that, remembering the destruction of Thornfield Hall. But Jane picked it up at once and said that she could now see in hindsight that the burning of Thornfield was not such a bad thing, that it was a violent cleansing of evil. She is still of a most philosophical and theological turn of mind.

And I believe it is important never to overlook the powerful strain of romanticism that runs deep in Jane's nature. This manifests in several ways, not least in her willingness to believe in supernatural forces, and her desire to construct the episodes of her life as legends and fairytales, sometimes dark, and sometimes light and beautiful. I am thinking in particular of the events retold in chapter twenty-eight, as they flow on from the last pages of the chapter before. In those last pages Jane has just said what she believes to be her last farewell to Edward, and she is unable to sleep. Her imagination transports her sleepless mind into scenes of childhood; she is back in the red-room. She sees a vision of a glorious white woman, moonlike, breaking through the clouds, and the woman speaks to her, calling her 'daughter', telling her to flee. And flee she does.

The fine details of this moment when Jane, the eighteen-year-old governess, recent bride-to-be of Edward Rochester, slips from the hope of comfort and prosperity to become a woman of the hedgerows, are exquisitely, painfully drawn. She makes up a parcel—some linen, a locket, a ring. In her purse she puts twenty shillings, and, carrying her slippers so as not to make a sound, she steals out. The image of her getting oil and a feather and oiling the key and lock so as not to make a noise has always seemed to me to be particularly poignant. 'Without one sound' she passes through the doorway. The great gate is locked, but little Jane, who seems as this moment to have no substance, opens a wicket and out she goes. This is the ritual of crossing the thresholds like a ghost. She uses the words 'deadly sad', and they are perfectly apt. Her past is a mixture of the deadly sad and the heavenly sweet; her future is 'an awful blank'. Of all the exits and entrances of Jane's life that the user can examine, this moment of flight is probably the most painful, and possibly the most powerful. It is when Jane, with all her possessions in her parcel, becomes that most helpless and vulnerable of creatures, the homeless woman, the vagabond, the beggar. She leaves behind the pearls that Edward gave her, since they belong to the 'visionary bride' who has now melted into air, and she herself, it seems, melts into air.

And because she feels that in her flight she has betrayed her beloved Edward, she hates herself, and the depths to which she briefly falls become a metaphor for that self-hatred. She knows herself to be the instrument of evil to the one she wholly loves. She falls in the mud, crawls forward, and spends all her money on a coach ride to take her as far away as possible. And so she comes to Whitcross, a white crossroad in her life. She has left behind in the coach her parcel of belongings, and so now she is utterly destitute.

She really is a pitiful beggar-woman. In a few days she has been stripped of the bridal finery, emblems of safety and success, and has taken on the bedraggled garb of the road where there are probably only two careers open to her, the thief and the whore. We'll have material here about modern women's refuges and homeless women at the end of the twentieth century. People are still buried in paupers' graves in modern cities, you know. The female psyche is still to some extent haunted by the fear of the bag-lady, the knowledge of how easy it is to slip below the surface of society and disappear. Jane's story ends differently because she stumbles, guided, she believes by God, into the haven of the home of St John Rivers.

As she wanders about getting more and more hungry and desperate, she characterises herself as a bird of the air, a biblical creature to whom God affords nourishment and nest. In the birds themselves the reader senses hope for Jane. She is guided by God, guarded by Nature. She nestles into the 'breast of the hill' and goes to sleep, hoping to die, to decay quietly and mingle with the earth. She wakes up and goes on. She hears a church bell, sweet announcement of her salvation. The sounds of birds, clocks and bells will be available on the CD-Rom, as they are underlying themes in the music of the narrative.

She tries to barter her silk scarf and her gloves for a piece of bread, but they are rejected; she begs the swill for the pigs. But eventually she sees 'a pretty little house' with 'a garden before it, exquisitely neat and brilliantly blooming'. The door is white, the knocker is glittering. I can't help thinking of mirage and hallucination brought on by starvation—things are too bright, too sudden, too sharp. But the householder is no help, the mirage fades. Finally Jane goes to the parsonage, only to learn that the parson is away, and she wanders off onto the moorland where she hopes to die, and where crows and ravens can pick her bones. This of course a thoroughly romantic version of what might happen. The light that finally leads her (Lead, Kindly Light) to the safety of St John and his sisters appears now, 'shining dim and constant through the rain'.

Rough stones, prickly hedge, and she finds a white gate, a wicket gate, the counterpart of the wicket by which she left when she left Thornfield Hall. She enters and there is the friendly gleam of the light, shining through—bliss—'the lozenged panes of a very small latticed *window*'.

What she sees through this window is pure cosy fairytale—no palace ever looked finer to a Cinderella than the parlour of this long, low house. The beacon of the candle, the *red* of the firelight, the walnut dresser with pewter plates, the clean, sanded floor, two ladies in deep mourning, a dog, a cat. And an elderly woman who is knitting a stocking. I suggested to Jane that at this point we might supply the user with a pattern for knitting a stocking, and she thought it was a good idea as many modern readers of the book and users of the CD-Rom would probably never have thought about this very important aspect of life in the time of the story, and the stocking is a detail that emphasises the warmth, simplicity, domesticity, safety and love of the house to which Jane has at last come.

The whole pattern with pictures and diagrams and explanations will be on the CD-Rom, but here is a sample: For one stocking you get eight ounces of four-ply and four no. 14 needles. Cast on eighty stitches, twenty-six on one needle and twenty-seven each on two other needles. Knit two, purl two all around for thirty rounds. Now begin the leg. Knit plain for eighty rounds. Then begin to decrease to shape the calf. Knit to within three stitches of the middle, slip one, knit one, draw the slipped stitch over, knit one, purl one, knit one, knit two together, knit the rest of the round plain. Knit eight rounds without decreasing, and then repeat the decrease row. Repeat this procedure eight times, reducing the number of stitches to sixty-three. Knit sixty-three rounds. After this you come to the heel, the foot and the toe, instructions for which will be on the CD-Rom.

To protect herself, to cut herself off from her past, Jane gives a false name to her saviours, and ironically, by not saying she is an Eyre, she conceals from them and herself for the time being the family link that exists between them all.

The homeless bird is, without knowing it, home. She is in the bosom, not of the Nature she so lately craved, but of her own family. I have spoken to Jane about the incredible coincidence of this fact, of how, of all the places she could stumble into she came here. She speaks of the guiding light, of the hand of God, of the wisdom of the moon itself, and she says also that because this is the way it happened, she has simply set it down as it was, and left the power of her words to convince the reader of her veracity. In a sense, she says, the facts are so fantastic that nobody would invent them.

We also discussed the way she lay in her bed and heard the Rivers comment on her, and how St John pronounced her plain to look at. I asked her how she felt about that, and she said it has never really troubled her, and that she has even felt her story to be more interesting and accessible to readers who can more easily identify with a plain character than with some great beauty. I said I thought that she might have even understated her own appearance, and she said that this was possible.

There's a point about her clothes. The black silk frock and the shoes and stockings she wore for the journey had been through a lot, and the sisters had restored them as best they could. This was a very nineteenth-century detail, I thought. Nowadays the easiest thing would be to get her some new things. Easier than cleaning up the old ones.

Life, for Jane, from this point on, is not free

of trials, but she is on an upward curve. She is restored to her old firm self, and is never again in danger of absolute homelessness. She establishes her selfhood immediately with the housekeeper, retaining a sense of mystery and integrity, making gooseberry pies, and becoming part of the domestic scene. She was surprised when I told her I had searched for a recipe for gooseberry pie in my many cookery books and had even e-mailed friends asking for help, and had been unable to find one. Gooseberry amber, cheese, chutney, cluster cup, cream, flan, fool, huff cap, jam, jelly, meringue, mould, pudding—but between moulds and puddings, no pie. Jane suggested I try the Net, and sure enough there was a recipe on the Pie Page (http://www.teleport.com/~psyched/pie/goose.html). At the home of the Rivers, the homeless, loveless orphan of the early years has taken her final great step towards the house, hearth, home she has always craved. I asked her whether anybody had ever made a board game of her life; she said she didn't know, but we agreed that it was a perfect blueprint for such a thing.

I recently received a glossy invitation to an exhibition of Jane's latest paintings. The pictures are vivid interiors, rooms filled with rich furnishings and all with windows looking out onto gardens, parks, and hillsides. The gallery, is, by nice coincidence, close to the Freud Museum in London. She has painted several pictures of Thornfield as she remembers it in the good times; and also some of the ruin. One of the great pleasures of making the CD-Rom will be the opportunity to publish a number of Jane's paintings to illustrate the text. She still has, by some miracle, the first pictures she showed to Edward so long ago. The drawings she imagined while trying to get to sleep at Lowood—freely pencilled houses and trees, butterflies hovering above over-blown roses, birds picking at ripe cherries—these can all now be found in her folio. There is also a series of beautiful and haunting sketches of Helen Burns, mostly from memory, although a few are works Jane did before Helen died.

I am keen to include a photograph of the plate on which Bessie brought Jane food after the ordeal in the red-room. Brightly-painted china with a bird of paradise nestling in a wreath of convolvulus and rosebuds. This plate, also, has survived unscathed. It's one of the many objects in Jane's story that testifies to her love of colourful, exotic trappings. She admits that she still feels a secret attraction for crimson velvets and glittering crystal, for exotic gifts from the Continent, and for the even wilder ornaments of the East and the Indies, but says she is now dedicated to moderation and simplicity. She had Adèle educated in England, she said, in order to correct her French defects.

Gulliver's Travels and *The Arabian Nights* and *Pilgrim's Progress* are still among her favourite books, showing her lifelong belief in the magic of storytelling and the dangers and pleasures of the traveller in strange and unknown lands. Demonstrating also the way she has always positioned herself powerfully at the centre of the story. She sits curled in the window-seat behind the red curtains, observing the icy, moonlit world outside, and spinning from her own imagination the story of the pilgrimage of her life. We'll definitely start the CD-Rom with the cliché of the closed red curtains, so inviting, like a theatre, so full of promise yet subtly infused with threat. What rooks, ravens, black phallic villains and scarlet goblins will come forth? When the curtain comes down at the end, what countries of the mind we shall have visited.

Jane sees the making of the CD-Rom as yet another pilgrimage, another following of the windings of an unknown road. I have recently sent her a copy of *The Wizard of Oz* which she had not read, but which she thought sounded very interesting. Meanwhile, I am working on the development of Jane's story in a form that she says she never imagined would be possible.

carmel.bird@c031.aone.net.au

It has not of course been possible for me to indicate in the text most of the places the user of the CD-Rom will be able to explore. Consequently I will list here some of the key words that will be highlighted for use, giving access to all manner of different forms of text, illustration, sound and walkthrough: red, black, white, window, gate, door, mahogany, moon, sun, fire, snow, house, homeless, pilgrim, Freud, Simone de Beauvoir, Thackeray, bride, raven, bird, rose, dream, stocking, gooseberry, clock, bell, eye, fairy.

My dearest Jane

AMY WITTING

Amy Witting was born in Annandale, an inner suburb of Sydney, in 1918. She attended Sydney University, then taught French and English in State schools. She has published three novels, *The Visit, I For Isobel*, and *A Change in the Lighting*; two collections of short stories, *Marriages* and *In and Out the Window*; two books of verse, *Travel Diary* and *Beauty is the Straw*, as well as numerous poems and short stories in magazines such as *Quadrant* and the *New Yorker*. She was awarded the Patrick White Prize in 1993.

Worthing Manor
3rd November, 1854

My dearest Jane,

I write this letter in a mood of bitterness, or rather in a passion of indignation against injustice which would do credit to my dear Jane herself.

I am under notice here. The young master, down now permanently from Oxford, has been paying me marked attentions—without, you may be sure, any encouragement from me! But his mamma chooses to believe otherwise and was quite open, to the point of insult, in giving me the reason for my dismissal.

So there the situation is. I am supposed to be attempting to entrap Mr Edmund—such a Puffer Fish, my dear, as no woman would wish to find entangled in her net!

No matter how plain my dress, nor how subdued my manners, I must suffer once more from that caprice of Nature which clothed me in a style quite unsuitable to my station in life. I know that it is most unbecoming in a woman to attribute beauty to her person, but I trust you, my dearest Jane, to hear without misjudging me.

I was so angry at the insolent accusation that I quite forgot to guard my tongue. 'Indeed, Madam,' I said, 'as an affectionate parent, you must wish to spare your son the pain of a rejection which must follow any proposal he might make to me!'

'You forget yourself, Miss!'—looking very much the mother of a Puffer Fish as she spoke.

'No, Madam. It is I who know what respect is owed to a virtuous female, and you who forget it! You forget yourself when you forget that!'

I was asked to leave at once, with a month's salary in lieu of notice. This was, I suppose, for the convenience of Master Edmund, for whose comfort I care not a jot. He glooms about, convinced that his heartless mamma stands between him and his happiness, a position in which I should be quite willing to stand, though the fatuous youth could never be brought to believe such heresy.

I have refused to budge. I shall not be thrown upon the world without a prospect of employment. I am applying for other positions while I continue my duties. At least there will be no heartbreak this time in leaving the children—cold, arrogant and priggish young ladies as they are, with hardly a trace of real childhood about them.

I have little hope of a good reference here. Meanwhile the Puffer Fish sulks, without one thought for the unfortunate young woman he has cast upon the world. How selfish are these animal passions to which those who hold them dare to give the name of love!

Forgive the bitterness of my tone, dear Jane, and write to comfort me!

I am glad that Thornfield Hall promises so well. Mrs Fairfax seems to be an amiable person, and the little French girl quite enchanting.

One thing, however, in the situation does disturb me. You speak of the strange manners and unprepossessing appearance of the servant Grace Poole, but you do not give an adequate reason for her employment in the house. Amiable Mrs Fairfax may be, but I think that she is withholding information which may affect your comfort and even your safety. Such a person, so withdrawn and yet given to this rowdiness, may easily be prone to excesses of rage, or of irrational behaviour. Are there not servants and sempstresses to be found, who can be relied on not to indulge in strange mutterings?

What an odd little person you are, my darling Jane, with a head full of fancies, of legends and goblins, for here is a mystery which I should be compelled to investigate, yet which you seem to accept with great composure.

Remember, dear Jane, that we have no natural protector, that we must look to ourselves for comfort and security. I beg you to inform yourself further about this woman's employment.

The problem is how to inform yourself, since a direct question to Mrs Fairfax will clearly bring a vague and unsatisfactory answer. The social standing of the governess is so precarious that to gossip with the servants may sink it altogether, yet what other source of information can be found?

You do not give me a full account of the staff. I do suggest that if you are reduced to seeking information there, you should avoid the upper servants, who are too close in situation to yourself. A ribbon or a pretty collar to the tweeny, a sixpenny piece to the bootboy, will compromise you less and may be just as productive. These young people are in general so neglected that the approach is in itself rewarding, even if it does not bring the reward of information. The selfless devotion of an under footman is quite beyond price, but cannot always be commanded.

I think I may write a manual, a 'Guide to the Governess in the House of the Mighty'.

But I shall not continue, for I know that these frivolities put you out of sympathy with me. I am not being frivolous, however, when I beg you to be observant. There is some mystery here, and mystery is ever a cause of unease—except, it seems, to one gentle, trusting little Jane Eyre!

I wait for the dear expression of your sympathy. Do not fail.

Your affectionate friend,

Mary Ann Wilson

Worthing Manor
18th November, 1854

My dearest Jane,

Thank you for your dear letter. Your indignation on my behalf is a great support to me in this cold and hostile place.

I am firmly resolved not to move until I have found employment, but I am beginning to fear that this may not be easy. I have applied twice for positions for which I felt I was qualified, received promising replies, and travelled to an interview which ended in specious excuses and polite rejection. Alas, that a woman should have so little confidence in the constancy of a husband or the chastity of a son! But I begin to think that there is more than the unintended insolence—I find no better word—of my address that discourages employers. I have had spiteful indications here of a worse cause, questions about my reasons for leaving previous positions, with an undertone of implication which does me no credit.

I know that the sufferings of poor Mrs Fordyce were worsened by her consciousness of the injustice she was forced to inflict on me in dismissing me from my post, an injustice she strove to mitigate by the grant of half a year's salary, and by strenuous efforts to find me a new and favourable situation.

'You know, Mary Ann,' she said falteringly, 'I must think of your welfare also.'

It is strange that a young woman employed mainly for her skill in languages should not be supposed to have at her command the means of rejecting unwanted advances! Yet I knew that in this the poor lady was clinging to a last remnant of pride, so I let the matter pass.

I must protest, dear Jane, at your remark that you are glad to be protected by the plainness and insignificance of your appearance from such trials as mine.

You are not plain nor by any means insignificant. Your features may not be striking, but there is nothing in them to repel, and when they are animated by any interest or affection which may be brought to shine in your quite beautiful eyes, they possess a charm which transcends physical beauty. You are well equipped to inspire love. Let that knowledge guide your conduct.

I remember those weeks at Lowood when we roamed the woods—freed, as I now recall with compunction, by the typhus epidemic which was bringing sickness and death to many of our companions. We were too young to dwell on the thought of death, nor had the atmosphere of that institution promoted the formation of friendships which might have taught us to grieve. So we roamed happily. You sat beside me on that white stone which rose in the centre of the beck—running barefoot through the water to reach it, and thinking then that we had discovered a small kingdom of our own where none could challenge us. It was a pastime somewhat undignified for one of my advanced years, but you took such pleasure in it that it delighted me too. There we sat, safe from the world, and I told you stories of Apsley Park, the great house, the great park, the grand people who visited there unaware that they were scrutinised without indulgence by the servants, whose comments I loved to repeat to you, and when I brought your solemn little face to laughter, I felt both proud and tender.

I think I had never had a real friend before; I had not, since my mother's early death, known such an affection. You could not have known how dear it was to me, nor how I suffered when your solitary grief over the death of Helen Burns removed you from me into a region of sorrow where I could not penetrate.

One must not of course criticise a saint, particularly a dead saint, yet I could not share your reverence for Helen Burns. Indeed, I must feel some sympathy with poor Miss Scatcherd, whose duty it was to impart both knowledge and orderly habits. To say, 'Yes, I have earned this punishment and must bear it with patience,' is an exasperating answer to punishment, which aims towards amendment. Helen never did make a serious effort towards amendment. She did not become more attentive, nor remember to tidy her drawers.

I discern, however, something in you, Jane, which is drawn always to the extreme. Helen Burns was a saint indeed. I shall not further insult your feeling for her, except to remark that there are pupils I should prefer to have in my class.

Please allow these remarks to pass—put them down to the bitterness of a disappointed affection, which at that time caused me suffering. My friendship for you is deeper, I think, than yours for me; I am not formed on that heroic scale which only can command all your love. I know that I have your truest affection when I am unfortunate, and that gives me a little ease in misfortune.

How sententious, how analytical I am today! Believe me, I am prepared to accept truth from you as I hope you accept it from me.

As for the rest of your letter and the other misfortunes you ascribe to me—it was, I suppose, disgraceful that any dependant of a noble house should have been sent to such an institution as Lowood was when first we knew it. You know, my dear, that there is on my birth that shadow which justifies any contempt, any neglect of the innocent issue of sin. Yet there are extenuating circumstances. Money was not plentiful at Apsley Park, for all its outward glory. The estate was much encumbered through the debts left by that dissolute Marquis to whom I must suppose I owe my being. While my parentage was never openly acknowledged in the family, I was nevertheless the living representative of his faults. Many a dark look was directed at me when they were mentioned.

My father had left no heir. The younger brother who succeeded to the title—an honourable and conscientious man—set about paying the debts which threatened ruin to the house. Land was sold; great oaks were felled, to the grief of all. The new Marquis sold his magnificent hunters, dismissed an idle and incompetent steward and undertook the management of the home farm himself. His first efforts at farming were greeted with pity and derision in the servants' hall, but through common sense and application, he mastered his new trade of gentleman farmer; as the supply of poultry eggs, milk, butter, fruit and vegetables to the kitchen improved in quantity and in quality, contempt gave way to respect and even to emulation. Mrs Bonner managed the kitchen with due regard to economy.

The Marchioness furthered the efforts of the Marquis. I fancy that, being a woman of severe disposition, she felt some satisfaction in imposing restrictions on her two daughters—perhaps to remind them that they were but daughters! There was no son of the house; the estate was entailed upon the heir to the title, a distant cousin named Robert Lorimer.

Her Ladyship's only anxiety was that the economies practised in the household should not damage the family's standing in the world. Economy was practised in stealth; it was never allowed to interfere with the duties of hospitality.

I did not, in these circumstances, regard my consignment to Lowood as an injustice. It was in the breast of the two young ladies, Letitia and Honoria, that the sense of injustice burned fiercely. They had but one maid to attend both—and she an untrained girl who had other duties in the household. This they felt to be a disgrace. They lamented most the loss of the smaller carriage, which had been kept for their use and now was sold 'for the benefit of Mr Lorimer'!

Indeed, the name of Mr Lorimer evoked the same black looks as were so often directed at me.

As for the hardships of Lowood—I took care not to mention them at Apsley Park. I endured cold and hunger without complaint there, for fear of being taken away, since I had decided early that education must be my resource. I could not be invited to share the lessons of their governess with the Ladies Letitia and Honoria (being, you understand, the Very Dishonourable Mary Ann), nor would I have wished to do so, since I had soon advanced far beyond their standard.

My parentage was no romantic dream, I assure you. In the servants' hall, which was then my true home at Apsley Park, the talk was all of my likeness to my infamous Papa. 'That turn of the head she has, it brings His Lordship right to life!' 'She has His Lordship's eyes.'

I have been forced to the conclusion that His Lordship's eyes, set in my innocent countenance, send an invitation to liberties which are foreign to my intentions. This, the only legacy I have from my late unlamented Papa, is not likely to advance my credit in the world. At times I envisage a Supreme Being who has a quite malicious sense of humour. But I must not shock you, dear Jane, for your friendship means much to me. I went once into the picture gallery seeking his likeness, but found only a family group where he figured as a half-grown boy, stiff and solemn, with no hint of the mischief to come.

I never suffered as you suffered in the home of your infamous aunt. There were no terrors, nothing like the terrible red-room, no bullies such as John Reed to torment me. Her Ladyship regarded me with cold dislike; my cousins—if I may take the liberty of claiming them as such—disliked me perhaps more intently, but were too conscious of their own dignity to ill-treat me.

Nor must I ever forget that my dear Mamma was not turned out to die in want. She was maintained by a pension from the family, so that I owe to their bounty nearly eight years of carefree childhood, and when my happy village life was ended by Mamma's early death, they gave me a home, food, clothing and education. Many people would have done less. It was perhaps heartless to leave me at Lowood during the typhus epidemic, but they had after all a great establishment in their charge and were responsible for the health of many. I cannot make a grievance of a neglect which brought me such a time of happiness.

Write again; tell me more of Thornfield—and what of Grace Poole? Is her behaviour still marked by outbursts of wild laughter and by strange mutterings? Have you given some thought to my advice? I wish with all my heart you would do so.

I shall continue my search for employment and tell you how I fare.

Your affectionate friend,

Mary Ann Wilson

Worthing Manor
5th December 1854

My dearest Jane,

Do not take my reproaches so much to heart! You are quite right; there is in me a lightness of manner, even an air of frivolity, perhaps, which makes it difficult to perceive the depth and sincerity of my affection. You say that it was not until we began to correspond that you knew my true nature. That I understand. It is only with pen in hand that I feel free to express my feelings. Perhaps my situation at Apsley Park, which required that I conceal anger and humiliation, has given to my demeanour a fashion which might pass for indifference. Indeed, I have often been compelled to cultivate indifference to slights against which I had no defence.

We understand each other better now, and I trust that you value my affection as I value yours.

You ask me why I do not take refuge at Apsley Park, where I must have a claim at least to shelter. Perhaps I shall do so as a last resort, though it would be to me a bitter confession of failure. I have told you that my early childhood there was not unhappy. Below stairs I was much petted. Below stairs I was 'His Lordship's little girl', while above stairs I was 'poor Wilson's child'.

In the servants' hall I was always welcome; it was home to me, but the kitchen was my delight. I spent my happiest hours in that bright, warm, active place—I cannot call it a room, since it had more the air of a busy market or workplace. I was lucky in the tolerance of Mrs Bonner. She had even bought for me from her own wages a miniature pastry board and roller, which I plied busily, making small tarts which Emily the kitchenmaid would put in the oven to bake. This was good training for a cook, and I might have grown to be a good one.

Unfortunately, as I acquired some of Mrs Bonner's skills, I was also acquiring her habits of speech. One afternoon I chanced to meet the Marquis as he crossed the hall and, on his kindly enquiring whether I was happy at Apsley, I answered blithely, 'As happy as a little pig in the muck pail, thank you, my Lord,' thereby pronouncing my own sentence of banishment from the kitchen.

When I arrived next morning, ready for the expected task of stalking the currants which had been brought in the day before from the kichen garden, I found Emily weeping and Mrs Bonner muttering from lips set in anger.

'You can't come here any more, Mary Ann,' said Emily. 'His Lordship says it's not right for you to play in the kitchen. So I'll have to find another kitchen maid for when I'm a cook.'

Mrs Bonner's muttering became louder and more intelligible. 'Too good to be a cook, that's the story. Too good to be a cook, but, mark my words, never good enough to be a lady. If those who have a feeling for the child aren't allowed to concern themselves, then who will, and what's to become of her? That is what I ask and I mean to have an answer from those who take it on themselves . . .'

At this temerity, her voice sank again to a mutter.

Her wrath was Jovian and her influence such—the influence of an excellent cook angry enough to give in her notice at the slightest further provocation is not to be ignored—that it reached above stairs and fetched down an answer. I paid one more visit to the kitchen, escorted by the housekeeper, who was nervous and flurried at facing righteous anger. She told Mrs Bonner, and incidentally myself, that I was to go to school, and that when I was at Apsley Park I was to eat my meals in the nursery wing with Mrs Field and the young ladies.

I should probably not have persisted in my ambition to become Emily's kitchen maid and her apprentice, on my way to becoming a cook, but the nursery wing was a poor substitute for the bright, bustling kitchen, and the company of Miss Field and the young ladies, who clearly resented the intrusion, very dull after the gossip and the laughter of the servants' hall. Miss Field particularly, being set, I think, to correct my speech, resented the task and performed it without concealing her resentment. The poor lady felt herself much compromised by her brush with my vulgarity.

The nursery wing of course no longer housed a nursery. It consisted of a schoolroom, a sitting-room where we took our meals, and a small bedroom which had once been occupied by the nursery maid and was now Miss Field's quarters and which later was mine.

Since my own experience as a governess has enlightened me, I understand how painful was Miss Field's experience. The social standing of the governess is in the gift of the employer. Miss

Field was given little honour and scant politeness by Her Ladyship, nor did Letitia or Honoria offer that open-hearted affection with which one's pupils can make the position tolerable in spite of slights from the household.

Exiled from the kitchen and left without occupation, I wandered into the library and discovered—with what joy and excitement—the world that was to be mine. Most of the text, of course, was beyond my small domain of literacy; I looked for books with illustrations, works of natural history and travel. It is so strange, to reflect that like you, I found Bewick's *History of British Birds*—but, unlike you, I did not linger on the coasts of Norway, which I found forbidding. There were pleasanter pictures to dwell on: a mother bird in its nest, a robin picking crumbs from a windowsill—my tastes, I fear, tended to the sentimental rather than the heroic.

I did apply myself to the text beneath the engravings and by spelling out and recognising a word here and there; I began to increase my power of reading and to look forward eagerly to the promised arrival at school.

I owed my entrance at Lowood to Lady Forrester, a friend of Her Ladyship who had contributed money to the institution and therefore had the privilege of granting a few places there. To Lady Forrester I was represented as the illegitimate child of a servant—which was of course true, and the whole truth if one accepts that a child has only one parent! I did not blame Her Ladyship for her discretion, but I did dislike the other's admiration of her charity. I was, however, too bent upon the prospect of education to harbour bitterness.

I suffered less than you did at Lowood, being older by two years, well grown and, I fear, aggressive. No one stole my half-slice of bread and, upon my honour, I never deprived a smaller child, although I see now that I did not do enough to protect the younger children—the struggle for survival makes one selfish, indeed.

Besides, I spent my vacations at Apsley Park, where Mrs Bonner set herself to fatten me for the lean term ahead.

'What they feed you in that place I do not know!' she would scold. Nor would I tell!

In those vacations, I was set to help Rachel the sempstress. Sewing, it seemed, was a genteel occupation, though laborious enough to make it a servitude.

Rachel was a quiet, well-looking woman of perhaps thirty, not so much a woman maturing as a pretty girl fading day by day. She worked at a long cutting-table in the sewing room, with no company but a headless, limbless figure of Her Ladyship, which I greeted every day with a curtsey and a compliment. 'Your Ladyship is in excellent looks today!', 'I doubt that I have ever seen Your Ladyship look better!'

The purpose of this childish habit was to make Rachel laugh, in which purpose it succeeded, though the little spurt of laughter was always followed by a protest. 'Mary Ann, you are wicked!', 'Mary Ann, you shouldn't say such things!' Yet a small smile lingered when the laugh was gone, so that I was encouraged to persist with my impertinent little ceremony.

It was in the sewing room that the art of keeping up appearances was most effectively combined with economy. Nothing was wasted; handsome trimmings of lace and fur were carefully unpicked and set aside to be used again. Her Ladyship's ball gowns came from a famous house in London, but, after a brief social life and a tactful lapse of time, they were cut again to make evening gowns for the young ladies. Unlike Her Ladyship, they were required to attend the sewing room for fittings, which they did without grace, for they found the contrivance humiliating.

I never acquired Rachel's skill with the needle. The stitching of a long seam, a day's work to me, was for her the work of an hour, and to see her beading a design was to watch a skill which approached artistry. I did, however, show a natural aptitude for cutting and design, and could adapt the master pattern to reproduce a fashion plate from the *Ladies' Journal*. There were times in the sewing room when the work went well and we were happy in our achievements, though they met with little appreciation from those for whom the gowns were made.

It was over the honey-coloured satin that I felt the first stirrings of rebellion on Rachel's account. It was cut as usual from a gown once worn by Her Ladyship. Rachel had gathered the bodice into a standing quilted collar and finished the full sleeves with cuffs of the same quilting. This quilting was Rachel's masterpiece. The great house in London could not have produced its equal, and when we called Lady Letitia for her fitting, we had a sense of anticipation, an expectation of giving pleasure which quite raised our spirits. Letitia however put on the gown without remark, except to say ill-temperedly to Honoria, who of course had accompanied her, 'All this to save a few fields for Mr Lorimer!'

Rachel turned away to hide a tear of mortification and I bit my lip to repress an angry comment. When they had departed, I asked Rachel why she gave herself so much trouble, since it was paid poorly in money and not at all in appreciation.

'But this is the part that I enjoy,' she said, stroking her quilting with a loving touch. 'I only wish, Mary Ann, that I was doing it for you!'

That was the only protest I ever heard from Rachel, but I began to ponder the difference between her condition and that of Mrs Bonner. They both had special skills; Rachel's perhaps were rarer, yet Mrs Bonner had authority, even some power, and certainly earned higher wages than Rachel, whose skills must save the family hundreds of guineas in a year. Mrs Bonner supported the prestige of the house, while Rachel was involved in its private embarrassments—but must the value of a woman's work be judged according to the caprice of others? Should it not have some absolute value, independent of the part it played in their lives?

I began to experience a discontent which was, for the first time, not selfish. Meanwhile, I had cause for selfish discontent. As first Letitia, then Honoria, left the schoolroom to take their place in society, and soon afterwards Miss Field moved to another situation. I was left alone in the nursery wing.

As I sat over my books at night, I heard the sounds of music and laughter from the drawing-room, and oh! how I longed to join that company! How much I resented my exclusion from a society to which I felt, nevertheless, that I belonged. A cold anger was growing in me, which, without my full understanding, was poisoning my tongue. Too often, in the sewing room, I lamented that a shade of sage or amethyst might be unkind to Letitia's complexion, or recommended a cut which might disguise Honoria's corpulence. One day I saw Honoria flinch, while Letitia's lip curved in scorn, and I perceived with shame that I was being possessed by a truly menial spite.

Small as my virtues are, I cling to them. I could endure Letitia's scorn, but not the deserving of it. At that moment, I resolved to leave Apsley Park for ever.

I sought an interview with the Marquis, and informed him that I had decided to make my way in the world as a governess, that therefore I wished to spend my vacations at Lowood, where I should take private lessons in French with Madame Pierrot, and also begin the study of Latin with the rector of the parish—I was, you see, ambitious!

'I think your place is here, Mary Ann,' he objected.

'And where in this house is my place, sir, since I belong neither in the servants' hall nor in the drawing-room?'

At this he nodded unhappily and gave me his blessing, asking only that he should always know where I was and what was my situation. I promised him this and have kept the promise, for I know that he will always be my friend and will help me in need.

So I left Apsley Park. The Marquis gave me twenty guineas, wincing a little at the smallness of the sum. Rachel wept and gave me an embroidered purse, at which I wept too, for since Mamma died, I had had no presents, except for

Mrs Bonner's pastry board and the guinea which I received from the Marquis at Christmas and on my birthday. The latter attention I appreciated very much. He had had to ask me for the date, and had given me my first guinea when he found that my eighth birthday had passed unremarked. That small kindness I have never forgotten.

Her Ladyship gave me an almost new mantle which Letitia had particularly disliked, and bade me remember the benefits I had received from the family. My answer to this had been well rehearsed, I assure you.

'Madam,' I said, 'that this family did not fail in its duty to my very dear Mamma is a circumstance which must always command my respect for its name.'

Having delivered this strictly limited measure of praise—which did a little curdle Her Ladyship's complexion—I curtseyed and departed.

I tend to forgive my enemies, since I find it the best and safest way of annoying them, but, having delivered my little shaft (long and lovingly polished, I admit), I usually succeed in forgetting them. Her Ladyship has not been much in my thoughts since then.

What a long answer this has been, dear Jane,

to your brief question: 'Why do you not take refuge at Apsley Park?'

I hope you have not found it tedious. To me, in the telling there have been some discoveries, some clearing of mist.

Let me have news of you soon!

Your affectionate friend,

Mary Ann

The White Hart
Worthing
20th December, 1854

My dearest Jane,

You will see from the above address that I have left the Manor. I could not endure to spend Christmas where the chill indoors, in spite of log fires, matched the chill without. I have received at this inn an unexpectedly warm welcome. The family at the Manor is not much loved in the village. Though I have said nothing of my reasons for leaving my employment there, it is taken for granted that it is through no fault of mine; indeed there is much unspoken sympathy for me. It seems that one of the inn servants, a pretty girl named Sarah, has a tale to tell of Mr Edmund.

I mean to have a happy Christmas. I shall go to church on Christmas morning and there try to find goodwill towards all, while I ask for guidance in directing my future. Then I have been promised a merry dinner at the inn, with the family and their guests, relatives from London.

As for my future—I have despaired of finding a new post as governess and mean now to look for employment in a school. I have a little money set aside, which gives me time for reflection.

Miss Temple warned me that I was not suited to the life of a governess. 'I know your qualities, my dear, and I value them,' she told me kindly. 'There is, however ... a little too much spirit in your address, which some might find challenging.' She did not mention His Lordship's beckoning eyes, which I seem to my misfortune to have inherited, but perhaps she had them also in mind.

I do not quite share your reverence for the virtues of Miss Temple, though I appreciated her kindness and enjoyed her instruction, which was indeed of the first quality. I thought myself lucky in the acquaintance, for all teachers are not so inspiring!

I came, however, to believe that in virtue she fell a little short. I know she defended you against a false accusation, taking a trouble that many would have neglected in your cause, and for that I honour her—yet she did not defend you to Mr Brocklehurst. She did not take that one step further, which would have made her truly heroic.

I cannot forget that in the vacation which followed the typhus epidemic, I was called down from the sewing room to attend Her Ladyship in the small sitting-room. She sat there alone with Lady Forrester—I believe I have told you that Lady Forrester had given money to Lowood and had arranged for my entrance there. The poor lady had suffered much grief over the death of the children during the epidemic, and some disgrace from her connection with the institution. She now sat, pale and red-eyed, languid from weeping, her head resting against the wing of her arm-chair, an image of desolation.

Her Ladyship spoke to me sharply. 'Mary Ann, why did you not inform us of these dread-ful conditions at Lowood? Surely it was your duty to speak of what you saw there!'

Much you would have cared, Milady, thought I, and stood mute.

Poor Lady Forrester roused herself then to take my part. 'Mary Ann cannot be blamed. Children are taught to be silent, to show respect and obedience to their elders. They are told they should be seen and not heard. How then can they be expected to speak against those who hold authority over them, when all their training tells them that it is a fault to do so?

'I cannot escape my responsibility. I have had a terrible lesson. I know now that it is not enough to give money—one must accompany it with care and concern, but were there no adults there, no teachers who observed this regime of semi-starvation and who could have spoken out?' she cried out with sudden indignation. 'Could they not have had some faith, that among the sponsors of Lowood, there would be those who would remedy such conditions, if they had known of them?'

She had shaken her head, then, tired by the outburst, and drooped once more against the wing of her chair.

I began to see in this a limit to Miss Temple's virtue. She had seen, had deplored, had mitigated where she could, but for all that, she had condoned. You may object that she had had no choice, but choice is something women must somehow acquire—I know not how; my thoughts in this are vague and confused. There was a word I was looking for, and have found and have begun to hate. The word is *compliance*.

If Rachel had taken her talents to one of the great dress houses of London, she might have fared worse, I know, for the conditions of women working at dressmaking were never good; yet in the act of choosing her fate there would have been some merit, as there was a failing in Miss Temple's unquestioning acceptance of Mr Brocklehurst's authority.

I know that I ask for miracles. We cannot change society, but could we not change women and their view of themselves a little?

You lament that I had never told you the darker aspect of my life at Apsley Park, but in those days, I hardly knew it myself. It is only in the foreshortening of time which memory brings that one sees such things clearly.

I hope that you will have the best and happiest Christmas possible. How good it must be, to have the companionship of a child! You will be able to share the joy of the Christmas season with little Adèle.

Your affectionate friend,

Mary Ann

White Hart
Worthing
30th January, 1855

My dearest Jane,

Thank you for your letter and your kind enquiries. You see that I am still at the White Hart, where I am feeling quite at home. I have, however, made a journey or two in pursuit of employment and have settled my future. I have even had some choice in the matter! But more of that later.

I had the most delightful Christmas. Having learned from Mrs Hagerty what dolls the little girls from London might possess, I made use of the skills I had acquired at Apsley Park to fashion frilled and embroidered pinafores for those miniature persons. For the baby boy I stitched a soft ball in bright colours—it was lucky that I had carried away my workbag with its scraps of material! Mrs Hagerty's sister was delighted with the baby's toy, and the little girls were so entranced by the pinafores that the five-year-old Sophie spent the afternoon sitting on my knee, while seven-year-old Catherine asked earnestly if I could make dolls' dresses too.

'That will be for next year, if Mary Ann will come to spend Christmas with us,' said Mrs Hagerty.

For that, I could have thrown my arms about her in gratitude. How precious is the offer of some continuity in the life of a wanderer!

To my astonishment, there were presents for me under the Christmas tree. Mr Hagerty had brought in a small fir tree in a tub, and our presents were set under it. It was a pretty sight, Mrs Hagerty having hung it with gilded walnuts and small confections baked in the shape of stars and fir trees. I had not seen this custom before. Mrs Hagerty's sister said that such a tree was set up for the royal children at Christmas, and that the fashion had been much taken up in London. When my name was called, I came to receive a small needle-case and a pin tray.

I had been to church in the morning, to celebrate Christmas in the true spirit, but I found as much sacred feeling at the inn, being taken in by strangers and given tokens of love, as I had found in the church. The family from the Manor was in the front pew, and I did in the spirit of Christmas succeed in shedding my anger, and prayed for their welfare, but with more effort and less joy than I found in holding little Sophie on my knee.

So, dear Jane, you have met Mr Rochester. From the detail in which you report that first encounter, it appears that the gentleman has roused your curiosity. It appears to me that Mr Rochester is very skilled in making himself interesting. This was the great game in the drawing-room at Apsley Park, where gentlemen strove to fascinate the ladies and ladies returned the compliment. Molly, the senior parlour maid, all sober deference when she waited on the nobility and their guests, was nevertheless an excellent mimic and would, with the help of Hugh the footman, repeat these scenes for us. There was no harm in these little manoeuvres, and the laughter in the servants' hall was kind. There are, however, those, among both sexes, who seek to be loved where they have no intention of loving. This is not listed as a sin in the catechism (unless it is bearing false witness), but I think it is a grave one.

There is no doubt that Mr Rochester seeks, perhaps simply from habit, to engage your attention. In the first place, he withholds his name, in a situation where any gentleman of proper manners would have introduced himself at once. But your Mr Rochester—how earnestly I hope that he is not your Mr Rochester!—must wrap himself in a little mystery, which will keep him in one's thoughts, for a time at least. Then, he asks about you—quite unnecessarily, for you had told him that you were the governess—of little Adèle, knowing well that she will repeat the conversation to you.

Oh, Jane, have a care! I know the depth and the tenacity of your passions!

As for Mr Rochester's reserve, his air of gloom and despondency: he may indeed be gnawed by some secret sorrow; he may on the other hand have found this an effective way of touching the heart, particularly a heart of such ready sympathy as your own.

I repeat, dear Jane, have a care! Mr Rochester may have the best of reasons for wishing to gain your affection (I have already tried to convince you that you greatly underestimate your powers of pleasing), but if he is such a monster of vanity as would wish to capture any impressionable heart, I fear for you. I fear not for your virtue, but for your happiness.

If you find my letter impertinent, please judge me by my intentions and forgive me.

As for my future—I have made a decision which must astonish you. I intend to return to Lowood. Through the good offices of the Marquis, to whom I had, as usual, reported my situation, I received the offer of a post in a fashionable academy for young ladies, but I had also written to the superintendent to ask if there were a vacancy at Lowood which I might fill. She too offered me a post, much inferior in salary and conditions of course to the other—but I think there is work for me to do at Lowood.

I wait for news of you, dearest Jane.

Your affectionate friend,

Mary Ann

May Heaven armour me against the charms of Mr Brocklehurst!

White Hart
Worthing
31st January, 1855

Dearest Jane,

I have but now given up my letter to the post, and I sit down to write to you again, though there is much to prepare for the move to Lowood on Monday next.

It weighs upon me so much that I have left untold the story of my own unfortunate love, for I know well the sufferings which can follow the indulgence of a liking which cannot come to good. Shame has kept me from speaking, for the object of my affections was a married man. I could never have set out to love such, and can feel no pride in telling the story, yet I believe it may help you—and here I am, after all, pen in hand and determined to tell all, in the hope that it will be of service to you.

The post which Mrs Fordyce had found for me was pleasant, but of short duration, Miss Elizabeth needing only a companion with whom she might converse in French and somewhat improve her knowledge of literature before she left at the beginning of the next year to continue her education at an academy in Switzerland. I went from there to the Maynard household, where my story begins.

Mrs Maynard was an invalid, a frail, pretty woman who had not recovered her health after the birth of Gerald, three years before—a horrendous ordeal which she was inclined to recount in detail, though I think the practice was damaging to her health. She kept to her room, and usually to her bed, served by a personal maid named Agatha, who was something of a dragon, determined to protect her mistress from all demands on her energy.

My charges were the two elder children, two daughters, Arabella and Louisa—though little Gerald, too, would escape from his nurse, Ellen, to sit on my knee and learn his letters. Arabella was nine years old, Louisa seven. Since they were still in the care of the nurse, I dined alone with Mr Maynard. This was at first a cause of some embarrassment to me, but there seemed to be no possibility of any closer relationship, for he viewed the world and those in it from a slight but perceptible distance. I did not at that time find him pleasing either in person or in character. He could not be called handsome; there was about him a sleekness and plumpness which forbade the epithet, and as for his character—I took his continual amiability to be the shield of a detachment which made him indifferent to others, and most of all to his unfortunate wife, who seemed to live surrounded by every comfort but the sympathy of her husband. He failed in no attention to her, visiting her morning and afternoon to enquire after her health, but his very cheerfulness of demeanour appeared to make light of the sufferings she recounted. Agatha, indeed, thought it an insult to her poor mistress; she would direct at his back such a look of indignation as might well have bored two holes in his jacket. I learned later that Mr Maynard had tried to persuade his wife to dismiss Agatha and that this had brought on such a deterioration in the poor lady's health that the subject could never be mentioned again.

I thought Mr Maynard had been harsh in the matter, considering with what devotion Agatha tended her mistress, yet I too began to feel misgivings about the wisdom of the association, when I asked Agatha at what time of the day it would be best to bring the girls on their daily visit to Mrs Maynard, and saw the suggestion—it was something more than a suggestion, for I had taken compliance for granted—rejected on the grounds that the children tired their mother. There was perhaps no place for little Gerald in a sickroom, but Arabella and Louisa were quiet, affectionate, well-mannered girls. I felt strongly that the company of such daughters could do nothing but good to a parent. I thought of protesting to Mr Maynard, but caution kept me silent. My protest might have seemed officious; this was not my concern, or was only my concern to the extent that the happiness of the girls might be affected. On reflection I saw that it was for their mother to demand their company, not for me to impose it.

I have never known a more promising child than Arabella—such delight in learning, such grasp of new ideas, such a capacious and accurate memory. Louisa, the younger sister, though less obviously gifted, had a sensitivity, a responsiveness which made her a delightful pupil, and Gerald at three showed the same readiness in learning his alphabet.

I begged of Mr Maynard that the education of the girls should be serious, not confined to the acquisition of a graceful hand and the accomplishments usually considered suitable for young ladies. I asked permission to introduce Arabella to the study of Latin, for I thought that to memorise its structures was an excellent discipline for a mind already giving promise of distinction.

I was astonished at the eagerness of his approval.

He said, 'If an intelligent woman cannot play a part in public affairs, her education should still make her a fit companion for those who do, able to listen with intelligent interest and give wise advice. Even in private life, a woman of cultivated mind raises the standard of conversation wherever she goes.'

The unusual animation of his tone made me feel that it reflected his own disappointment. Perhaps, I thought, his unruffled amiability was a shield, not for detachment, but for despair, and I saw in him a temperament which somewhat resembled my own.

He began to pay visits to the schoolroom, to show the little girls an affectionate attention which had until then been lacking in their lives, all Ellen's affections being centred on little Gerald. We agreed so well in matters of education—his only care being that I should not be too ambitious for the girls, that I should leave them what he called 'a little space for discovery'. I had somewhat sinned in this respect and found the advice wise.

Such an ease grew between us in our discussions that I began to talk to him of my life at Apsley Park, of Lowood and the scandal of the typhus, of Lady Forrester and her grievance and when I mentioned the circumstances of my birth, I saw him give a small, confirmatory nod, as if he had seen in me some signs of aristocratic blood.

And there, dear Jane, was the first sign of danger, in my being so gratified by the discovery that he had speculated on the subject.

When first he put a careless hand on my waist, I put it away quickly, saying, 'Sir, you forget yourself.'

'Oh, no, Miss Mary Ann,' he answered with his usual calm. 'I never forget myself. I am always the object of my most tender concern.'

At that, I smiled. I was aware that, though my words had rebuked him, my flesh had not. So I knew my danger and knew that I should flee it. This is to tell a woman benumbed with cold that she must stay far from the hearth because fire can burn. Is there not that lovely space of warmth and light where one can see no danger? We resumed our normal conversation, our plans for the girls. I hoped that the incident had had no meaning.

One day, he called me into his office, to tell me, regretfully, that I must not allow Gerald into the schoolroom, for Ellen complained that I was destroying her influence over the little boy. I objected that he was never there for long, being too young for more than a quarter of an hour's attention to his letters.

'I am afraid that we must respect Ellen's wishes, since Gerald is under her authority.'

'As I am under yours, sir!' I answered rather tartly, as I was vexed by the prohibition.

'Is that so, Miss Mary Ann? Then I bid you to come sit on my knee.'

'I was not employed to undertake such tasks as that, sir.'

'Oh, it would be a task then, would it?'

'An onerous one, sir, and quite outside my duties as governess.'

But at the word 'task' he had looked so comically woebegone that I felt a smile tugging at my mouth.

I condemn Mr Rochester for playing on the affections of an unprotected young woman to whom he stands in the responsible relation of employer, yet I found the same conduct pardonable in Mr Maynard.

And still I stayed! Oh, I deserve all the miseries that followed!

How laughter undermines the principles of morality. I see it as a bright, strong tide washing against the walls that prudence and decorum erect against chaos. My very resistance became an amusement; I could delude myself that this was harmless teasing. You and I should have exchanged temptations, my dear Jane. You would have been repelled by Mr Maynard's frivolity, while I think I could deal briskly with your Mr Rochester!

Of course the day came which must come: he called me into his office and said, 'Mary Ann, we must think of the future. We must live together or apart.'

Speaking with unusual earnestness, he told me that he could not offer marriage, but could make such a settlement as would give me security in the event of his defection—or his death, which he said would be the likelier.

I said in a whisper that it could not be. I felt all the weight of my guilt at that moment.

'Think, my dear. What would be changed, except that I should be happy, and you too, I think. I believe you are not indifferent to me.'

At that, I nodded. I had begun to weep. In my bitter tears he knew his answer, yet he continued to persuade.

'Our happiness could be our secret; everything else could go on as before.'

Even at that moment of deep emotion, I paused to wonder at the simplicity of this. Could he suppose that in a house full of servants such a secret could be kept? If the gentry and the nobility suspected how much their servants knew about them and with what detached amusement they held such knowledge, I believe the social order would begin to crumble.

The thought had steadied me a little. There had been no doubt of my answer; if my father's blood had prompted licence, my mother's fate enjoined prudence.

'Where one thing changes,' I answered, 'all things must change.'

It occurred to me that what we were contemplating was pure evil. If one resigns one's life to the guidance of a passion, where might that passion lead? First to the betrayal of that poor invalid, and then? Could I be brought to hate a human being who had done me no harm, perhaps to the point of wishing her dead?

It shocked me then as it shocks me still, that evil could have worn so fair a face. With more firmness, I said, 'This must never be spoken of again. We have been wrong in indulging our liking so long. We must do so no more.'

'Then, Mary Ann, I think we must part.'

I nodded, being unable to speak for weeping.

At last I said, 'Give me two days, to say goodbye to the girls and to pack my belongings. I shall stay no longer.'

We dined together, but we did not speak again until we said goodbye. He said, 'I shall supervise the education of the girls.'

I thanked him and contrived to smile.

'At least, my dear one, let me try to protect you from want,' he said as he handed me an envelope, which I found later to contain a draft on his banker for a sum of money which I could not have accepted from any other man.

Oh, Jane! Despite all the suffering, the longing and the loneliness which have been the penalty of my self-indulgence, I hope I may live to see in a man's eyes again such steadfast tenderness, such infinite goodwill!

What am I saying? Am I saying that, for all the unhappiness it may bring, it is worth all, to have seen love in a man's eyes, to know that love exists?

This is not the advice I intended to give you.

(*Letter unfinished. Unposted.*)

Lowood
8th April, 1855

My dearest Jane,

It is so long since you have written, that I fear you may be ill or have met with some other misfortune which prevents you from writing to me.

I have another fear, that I may have given offence—it is my misfortune sometimes to speak with apparent levity where my feelings are truly engaged.

If this is so, and you feel yourself offended, please forgive me and let me have news of you, at least to tell me how I have offended.

Your affectionate friend,

Mary Ann

Lowood
1st May, 1855

My dearest Jane,

I see, by your impassioned defence of Mr Rochester, that I have indeed offended! Yet I must cling to my opinion.

I know you, Jane. You do not love where your love is not invited. I know from what you have told me in your letters that Mr Rochester has set out from the first moment to engage your affection in a manner quite improper to an employer. If he had any other motive than sheer mischievous vanity, then there is some mystery here which I cannot penetrate. And that may be so, for it is difficult to believe that you would be captured by such a one as I must think him.

Since you are offended by my judgment of Mr Rochester, and I am, I must confess, angered by your humble opinion of your dear self, I think that we must for the time being correspond no more.

Jane—here perhaps I give further offence, yet friendship compels me to it—if ever you need a refuge, there is a bed to be shared at Lowood.

I get on very comfortably with the superintendent, Augusta Lingard. We agree on many points concerning the education of girls. I know she would welcome you.

If your situation changes, if you have news for me, please write to me. Until then, let there be silence between us—a loving silence, for my part. I wait hopefully for you to break it.

Your affectionate friend for ever,

Mary Ann

THE LANDSCAPE OF FATHER LOVERS

MORAG FRASER

Morag Fraser is the editor of *Eureka Street*, a Jesuit monthly magazine of public affairs, theology and the arts. Her most recent book is *Save Our ABC: The Case For Maintaining the National Broadcaster*, edited with Joseph O'Reilly.

Siren Voices

Children can feel, but they cannot analyse their feelings; and if the analysis is partially effected in thought, they know not how to express the result in the process of words.

The chamber looked such a bright little place to me as the sun shone in between the gay blue chintz curtains, showing papered walls and a carpeted floor, so unlike the bare planks and stained plaster of Lowood, that my spirits rose at the view. Externals have a great effect on the young.

Jane Eyre

For three years it's family and sky and saltwater and buffalo grass that prickles your bare legs when the Adelaide heat drives us all out to sleep on the front lawn in the warm fug of fathermotherbrother.

Then the shell breaks.

Violet's voice is my first memory of assault from outside. It used to pulse, disembodied, down the black phone in the kitchen where we'd huddle every Christmas Eve, taking turns. The intimacy was startling. She called me darling in a voice that was familial but so beautiful I was alarmed. Honey and burr, with back vowels that were effortless. I used to think that anyone who sounded like her must be able to mean more than we could. She had range, she had landscape in her throat and tongue, and I was mysteriously connected to her.

My family was close, even secretive, so I was never told much about Violet. All I had of her were the expectations that a child builds out of fragments. She would telephone at Christmas and of course my father would speak first while my mother waited, and his voice would thicken to Violet's, his rhythms rebuilding the world he had left behind as a boy of eighteen but never relinquished. I was hypnotised by the way his mouth would refit itself to these more strenuous sounds: Scotland, like France and China, shapes the face. I imagined Vi pursing her mouth into a mirror image of her brother's and then twisting it into the smile of wry conspiracy that is the visa of the Highlands.

When I was old enough to draw links I imagined that Cleopatra must have sounded like Auntie Vi. I'd seen photographs of them both: Violet at a ball in the Sudan, a hunting tartan sash slung like a ceremonial pelt across her breast and pinned at the shoulder. Cleopatra lived in my *Arthur Mee's Encyclopædia*; perhaps she was really Sarah Bernhardt, languorous on a couch, draped in a plaid turban, but she had Vi's Edwardian face, with its long jaw and topaz eyes. My face. I own Violet's sash now. It was sent to me after her funeral, its silk creases worn into rents and the puncture marks of the great brooch still sharp in it.

My father's family are dark, tall as Masai but ponderous, not lithe. They don't swivel or spin or skip because to do so, you'd think, would bring the cairns crashing down. Their walk has the undeviating gravity of bleak religion. Expatriation is their way of being. So for twenty years Vi's malted contralto rang out at me from Cairo, or Suez or Khartoum. There was always a wind in the airwaves. And because Christmas Eve was also my birthday she was pitched, I believe, especially for me. I used to wonder if this woman, this sister of my father, ever had need of shouting because she could work spells enough with that sling-shot tone. Enclosed in the sound of her, I had the apprehensive certainty of being loved.

When I was twenty-eight I rang Violet from London. With strangers we are self-possessed—it's a mask this inward family burnishes assiduously. With her I was jagged and tongue shy.

'I'm coming,' I said. 'I'm here. May I come? I want to. I'd really like to . . . I want to see you at last.'

She was in Inverness, home because her husband was dead.

'Of course. Of course you must come,' she said. 'Don't drive in because you'll lose your way. I'll meet you out at Daviot.'

And she did meet me, in a pitching wind, up on the slant of the hill well short of Inverness. I thought we'd go home and grow easy in one another's company but instead she drove to Culloden and showed me the stone that has our name carved into it. It lay at an odd angle to the earth, as though it made no peace with gravity. I didn't know what to say to her. We walked up and down the field, our footfalls dead in the peaty litter from the pine trees that were planted long after William and his Redcoats had left it a butcher's pit. Culloden is muffled hell.

We drove through the old town and up Castle Hill to Violet's house, tucked in at the end of a battleaxe drive and flanked by the tallest trees I had ever seen. Perhaps they were maples. I forget now, but at the time she told me all those things. I remember the leaves because the translucent sheen of a northern spring was on them and they made me edgy. I expect endurance from leaves, not fragile, profligate display. But they were beautiful. So beautiful, I babbled, and Violet grew gracious. She confided to me all the advantages of the odd sub-division—the privacy, good neighbours, the lie of the land.

'Take it all in. Your father lived here a wee while.'

She gestured grandly. The proud chatelaine.

Inside we gossiped and exclaimed and drank tea and whisky. Violet kept two giant Dobermans who flinched obediently at her diphthongs. 'No-ooa,' she murmured, to keep them at the edges of our games. We moved from room to room. Violet pulled hats out of cupboards and we tried them on. Neither of us has the face for hats but she went to the Church of Scotland down along the Loch and had a keen sense of the proprieties so she gave me a scarlet cashmere shawl and I wore that. We dug about in corners. Violet unclipped a hidden ladder so we could climb up into the attic and look at relics. My father's photographs were all dated from the year that he went to sea. He had only sisters.

'We loved him terribly, you realise.'

I didn't know whether I was being reproached or initiated.

Downstairs in the drawing room I was propped with a sherry while Violet boiled sheep's heads for the dogs on the great Aga in the kitchen. She did a week's worth all at once, in huge vats.

'Don't you come in here,' she instructed. 'They smell dreadful. No-ooa. Stay out.'

She was right about the acrid stink of flesh boiling off bone, but I would have liked to help her, to have mucked in, chopped and cleaved and become implicated. Instead I meandered around the chill room looking at photographs and colonial souvenirs. My father was here too, shrined on the sideboard, in the familiar photograph we all owned because we loved the glamour of his ironic youth and the tilt of his peaked cap.

Next to him on the starched linen runner lay a weighty rectangle of clear polished resin. A paperweight maybe, brought back from the desert—we didn't ask about things like that, even when curiosity stretched endurance. I picked it up and tilted the block toward the light. There was a scorpion suspended in it.

When I went back again in November the trees were the colour of running foxes and Violet was cagey. Something had happened.

We visited a cousin for afternoon tea. Fruitcake, shortbread, salmon on crustless bread. When Cassandra left the room to fetch scones hot from the stove, Violet pointed to the chairs ranged around the edges of the table. There were sixteen, scrolled and delicate, with a whiff of powder and wig about them. I was too routinely itinerant to take much heed of chairs. The diaspora had made at least one aspect of tribal snobbery obsolete I thought. But I noticed wood because my father and grandfather had worked it, with me as a child perched up on the bench watching them, breathing in the resinous tang of shavings and snatching the cedar peel as it curled away from my father's plane. Jarrah was the most beautiful wood but it broke my grandfather's drill and made him curse. These chairs, in their fluted elegance, were remote from any Australian carpenter's shed I knew.

'By rights they should be yours,' Violet declared.

And by rights I might well stand in a direct line of descent from Robert the Bruce and have the wits to say to you, Violet, that this is all ingrown nonsense.

That is how I would like our exchange to have gone. But Cassandra came back in a flurry of tea cloths and affection and I was left dumb, pondering what blood rituals bound me to mere furniture when all the linkages that dignified inheritance had rusted out.

'You remember going up to visit the grave with me?' Violet asked, after dinner. We'd eaten venison. She didn't meet my eyes.

'Of course.'

No one sensate could have forgotten. The graveyard hung off the side of a gravelly hill, its headstones leaning sheer out into the wind. It was a goat's climb and Violet was not supple, but we'd gone, I think, because she wanted me to see where her husband was buried. The house carried traces of her other life with him, but it was the only time we mentioned him at all. We never mentioned her father, my paternal grandfather. None of us did. Ever.

She poured more wine and looked across me. The room froze.

'I found this on the ledge at the back of the grave,' she said. She handed me a gay leather sewing kit stamped with daisies and garish cornflowers, threads looping out of it. I'd lost it months ago. God knows where. It was a degenerated piece of late industrial trash that I carried, for lack of anything better, to keep my hems free of safety pins. It didn't matter.

'I thought you must have put it there deliberately, to insult me.'

Her perfect voice measured out the syllables in tight clumps.

'It was ... like a desecration ... to find it there.'

Her face set. But I knew that face from the inside. It was the one I'd dreaded and learned all my childhood, the face with wit drained out of it and clamps put on all its passages. She was madly wrong but I had no words to tell her so. In the world we had broached, denial was irrelevant, it was feeble, frivolous even. Violet and I were underground together, in the clawing ordeals of love.

We were quiet enough and gentle with one another the next day. When I went back to London she saw me to the train and told me how kind I'd been to come, and how like Roy I looked. (She had her own name for my father. They all did.)

How kind. Of kind. Humankind. 'How kind of you to let me come.' Bernard Shaw has wrecked the word for us.

Violet was not a gorgon. Nor was she my fairy godmother. She never had been. But we build these fairy monster women out of hurt and need and in return they make malevolent elves and thwarted lovers out of us.

I spoke to her once more, eight years later.

'No, you cannot come this time,' she told me. Even her voice was raspy.

'I've been ill. I wouldn't be able to do things the way I'd like for you.'

'Well may I at least come and visit you? Do something to help? I could cook . . .'

'No. Not this time. Next time.'

A week later I rang home to my father—twelve thousand miles away—to tell him that Violet had got up to answer the phone and had fallen as she walked back to her bed. She was dead when they found her the next day. He said nothing, and in our miserable silence we clung to one another.

Gargoyles

> Yet I had not forgotten his faults: indeed I could not, for he brought them frequently before me. He was proud, sardonic, harsh to inferiority of every description: in my secret soul I knew that his great kindness to me was balanced by unjust severity to many others. He was moody too, unaccountably so . . .
>
> St John looks quiet, Jane; but he hides a fever in his vitals. You would think him gentle, yet in some things he is inexorable as death.
>
> *Jane Eyre*

Inexorable was a word we used to play games with. It was one of our kitchen favourites, an escapee from the *Oxford-Websters-Brewers-Pears Encyclopædia* that cluttered the side table. The reference section, the bane of meal times, was a family joke, and the evidence we summoned to convict my father of having more than a touch of the dominie in him. His feminine streak we called it—it was powerful—and it came out in pedagogy.

He liked to add an extra syllable to the word and tumble it off his tongue. 'In-ex-olorable!' That was how old Sam the crofter who lived just below the big house in the Port used to say it. Or so he claimed. But we knew that was a bluff. He chanted the word for pure pleasure.

'How in-tol-erable to be in-ex-olorable!'

He must have loved his schooling, I thought, when I thought at all about what it was that formed a father. Most days he was as much a given as air.

I was home briefly after he finally retired from the sea. He'd strung it out, going back as skipper on the China route after he'd wound up as a pilot in Melbourne. My mother went with him. That shook the myths out of maritime adventure. Not that my father had even been a romanticiser. His world was too circumscribed by charts, navigational imperatives and the iron regimens of a master's responsibility.

When I was a young woman he had given me his papers to take care of during one unusually long spell up north. A modest wad of documents in a camphor wood box. References, certificates, old passports, letters of commendation. They were tied in bundles with frayed ribbon, some of it mine, preserved more for thrift than sentiment—that is how I will argue it. They were in characteristically perfect order. I had his permission, but still it was disconcerting—like cutting the painter—to read this man my father through the formal testimonials of strangers. I'd heard enough, hanging around boatsheds as an observant child, to know that men thought variously of him. He was exacting, he could be unforgiving. Some men were afraid of him. Others, like the sailors who arrived intermittently at our dinner table, spoke of him with the sardonic affection of men who'd shared a life. They were expansive, they told stories. One was an enchanter and his eyes were different colours. His name was Bill Escudia and he brought me coins with camels and pyramids on them and holes through the centre. I hoarded them in a Benson and Hedges cigarette box that I keep by me still to prove that he was real. The history in the camphor wood box was more prosaic. My father had passed all his tickets, from mate to master mariner. He was qualified to pilot vessels of unspecified tonnage through dangerous waters. He was a man of sober habits. The last sentence recurred so often I began to wonder at the roundabout complexity of maritime codes.

Now we sat at work, grown woman and old man, in separate rooms at opposite ends of the house. My mother had gone out to play the organ and he was angry with her. Music caused a firestorm in my father. Every bitterness he'd buried could be summoned by it. Once I found him on our back doorstep, speechless, breaking records over his knee.

Now, even at a distance of four rooms I could hear the ominous uptake of breath that we had learned to dread as children.

Shut down the reactive pulse. Turn resolutely to my desk.

The reference shelf, much expanded since our childhood, had migrated over. I was on a hunt for grotesques. An article on Umberto Eco's *The Name of the Rose* lay in front of me, black squares where the illustrations should have been. I riffled through engravings of every demonic freak on the bosses and drain spouts of Notre Dame and Chartres. Subtlety wasn't apt: Eco's distorted monks were allegorical types, their furies branded on their faces. William of Baskerville's ironic rationality, on the other hand, was too mercurial to fix in an image, although I knew its mental contours well enough. Up in the front room, a few paces from me, sat a specimen of fully functioning ironic rationality which had chosen to turn itself to stone. Stupid. Perverse. I took wicked pleasure in refiguring my father as blind Jorge driven to immolation in his labyrinth for refusing to say Christ laughed. Or sang. Or played the organ. I gave him the mask, mouth dragged to its chin and eyes crazed-white, of Thomas Wyatt's fifteenth-century hard man who dies not knowing himself, 'dazed with dreadful face'.

That was cathartic. For a couple of minutes.

I had to tell him what I'd done so I crept out and offered a cup of tea. Rituals. We talked around the edges of trouble, conscious both of the sharp pleasure of being together. We had an abrasive, tacit code, adapted for intimacy. He showed me a small table he'd been making for me, and I held it rigid for him while he tightened the screws. Both of us knew how delicate our bubble world was. We fell into a long silence. Speeches formed in my head, and in rehearsing a passionate ascendancy for my mother I confused the roles of woman and daughter.

'You are behaving appallingly.'

I stopped, shocked by my own temerity. His eyes glittered. We'd never done this before.

'You cause her such hurt. And for no reason that matters, except to your own pride.'

'She should be here.'

It was all he said. His face was black and terrible.

We'd drunk the tea. I made a second pot. We sat over it for an hour—it was a dreadful stew, but he didn't care about the taste of things. Years at sea had brutalised his taste. It was growing dark. She would be home soon. I wanted an end. I went back at it, too angry to be wise.

'Why, why do you do it? You know what joy playing gives her. It gives everyone joy. God knows, it takes nothing from you. She'd never take anything away from you. Why do you make it such hell?'

'I want her here.'

He was very grave now. I remembered fragments of rhyme he'd drummed into me as a child. 'Thoughts unexpressed may sometimes fall back dead ...' When I came, late, to read Ecclesiastes, it was weirdly déjà vu. My father had the Old Testament by heart, mingled with a great stock of even more pragmatic local lore. I was the one with the literary education and I should have traded, should have told him we were pitting our wills against one another and that could lead only to the rock face. But I didn't.

'No! You mustn't do this. You mustn't. It's wrong. I swear it's wrong.'

He swayed back. For one still moment I thought he was going to strike. Then his arms went out and hauled me hard against his heart.

'I know.'

And he shook with what I knew was terror.

The Bathing Club

> As to St John Rivers, he left England: he went to India. He entered on the path he had marked for himself; he pursues it still. A more resolute, indefatigable pioneer never wrought amidst rocks and dangers. Firm, faithful, and devoted; full of energy, and zeal, and truth, he labours for his race: he clears their painful way to improvement; he hews down like a giant the prejudices of creed and caste that encumber it.
>
> *Jane Eyre*

'India? Don't be ridiculous, woman. You can't go to India. It's a terrible mess. You'll catch your death of malaria.'

He wasn't on strong ground and we both knew it.

'I'm as fit as a mallee bull, and anyway, where were you on your twenty-first birthday—sick as a dog with black fever in some sump of a port gaol in Rio.'

The P & O vessel *Orsova* pitched its way out through the Heads and I stood on deck and watched the thick figure silhouetted on the bridge. Then I watched his broad forearms carry his weight down the swaying rope ladder at the ship's side and into the launch that took him away.

My hotel in Bombay lay on one side of a grand esplanade. On the other lay the Arabian Sea. It was sluggish and stained, the colour of pumice. He'd been right about trouble, but it was politics not parasites: India was in a state of turmoil, with Shastri dead so recently that the funerary garlands of marigolds still littered the narrow streets and bazaars and trailed like lightning off every balcony. I was as unprepared for the tumult of colour as I was for the political unease of the interregnum. But Bombay, not even an ancient city, seemed inured to strife. It absorbed it with the angled shake of the head that signifies assent of a kind—*acha*—and bemused me when it did not leave me feeling inept. No small translation problem, this one: I'd learned on the first day that the sideways head shake meant yes, not no. But the gesture was also a volume of Indian philosophy with a subtext of determinism. It meant yes and maybe, and maybe not, and excuse me but what an impatient fool you are to expect absolutes.

Every time I said *acha* I felt like a bad actor.

I spent four days in a missionary hostel, parked there by Indian friends who knew the managers and knew also that in this sprawling, down-at-heel old mansion there were some spare trestle-beds to be had. People were polite and helpful but there was a stringency about their good works that sat oddly with the splayed opulence and mango courtyards of the place. I knew very quickly I was there under false pretences. They had work to do. They spoke only as much Hindi or Marathi as was necessary. They had little patience with speculation. When I went looking for help with my *acha* problem I realised I was wasting their time. Imponderables were for dilettantes. At night, when they were all in bed, I tracked round and round the balcony to feel the worn, warm marble under my bare feet. It was like discovering quartz for the first time, or the glass from Southern wrecks, polished into medallions by the waters of the ocean that had lapped my childhood.

I thanked them and moved. And moved again, gathering as I went. Kind girls with deft fingers showed me how to pleat the front of a sari while their brothers scooped up the spare silk yardage and scurried me off to the best tailor in Byculla, the cheapest tailor, the one they always went to with their mother, their sisters and their Auntie Mona, to have the scant arm's length of cobwebby fabric made into a *coli*. They were curiously particular, different from the stark men I had grown up with; they had strong views about the right sleeve length for my *coli* and exactly how much midriff should show. They danced and twirled in a flurry of fraternal hospitality.

Their father, an old man fixed in his routines of austere privilege, would invite me to dine with him in the evening. He was a doctor, famous in Bombay. He took me with him on his rounds and into the operating theatre of his charity hospital. I watched him perform a hysterectomy on a slight girl, a prostitute. She seemed half my size. He wouldn't tell me what might happen to her afterwards. I was always out of proportion in India.

At night we would sit on the balcony of his private apartments and he would tell me, each time, that the salad was grown especially in his gardens so I should not worry that it was not clean. He taught me new cautions and an unfamiliar courtliness. He would turn the steaming bowl of prawns towards me and spoon out the best, dripping its milky gold masala onto my rice. His sons-in-law would come in succession to make their formal bows of goodnight. I wondered, silently, at their patterned deference, but with the old man I shared the strange and vocal intimacy of the traveller. He had lived in many countries. We had remnants of colonialism in common. We could be ironic together and laugh. But I was not his daughter.

In the hotel I was surrounded by familiar strangers. The two men who kept the keys were ritually polite and if they looked askance at this young Western woman living alone in a hotel on the sea front they did so discreetly. It took me months to realise that they knew my every movement and the name and calling of my every guest. They were unfailingly courteous and we did not understand one another.

I met a political Sikh, not one of the madmen who would later turn the Golden Temple at Amritsar into a blood site, but a safe and wily character who taught me Bombay and India from the front seat of his motor bike. I clung behind, lapping it all up. He told me—and

I understood him—that there was only a brief time in which we two could live like this, before the monsoon came. So early in the morning or at dusk we criss-crossed the city, reading its geography and its politics and occasionally its compromised beauty. You have to see the necklace of the Bay from the top of Malabar Hill, Bul Bul said. So we did. This is where the parathas are silkiest he promised. So we ate there. We looked at paintings together. He took me to meetings. He warned me to keep clear of his brother—not a man to be trusted with a young woman he said.

Bul Bul had established very early that I was not a mistress for him. When I fell asleep on his divan, as I did sometimes after a long ride, he covered me with the cotton rug from his bed, and, once, woke me gently at dawn to say that he didn't mind my being there but this was the dhobi's morning and the dhobi would be mortified if he had to sort the week's washing with a young woman in the room.

He laughed at my chafing impatience with India. I had a sweeper. Or my hotel had a sweeper, but I came to think of him as mine because I could not solve him and I could not help him. We didn't speak the same language, but that hardly mattered in a country where gesture is eloquent. What mattered was that I stood nearly six foot straight and he shuffled, jack-knifed by his trade and caste. His broom was no longer than his arm and his limbs had moulded to it. I used to clean everything in my tiny rooms before he came, in a foolish attempt to make us equals. He would look anxious and scour harder than ever. For days I was cruel enough to try smiling, talking and moving chairs out of his way. Be quiet and leave money for him, Bul Bul said. But later he took me to the lane that ran between the first and second nine of the Bombay Golf Club and showed me the huge dumped sewerage pipes where the sweepers lived.

Years later I saw him again, this man who became my brother. The BBC was interviewing a panel of senior advisors and journalists who had survived the Nehru/Gandhi dynasty and were now looking at the new disposition of India under the threat of fundamentalist politics. There he sat, his unturbanned hair still black and his conversation as urbane, droll and sage as I remembered it.

Bul Bul had dignified my days with explanation. Another Indian man filled them with stories, and I fell in love with him for it. I listened and was beguiled and yearned. But he was elusive and I was raw. I lost tolerance one late afternoon, waiting for him, and pinned a bitter note to my door. No names, just anger sharply coded. I thought a blind man would feel the scorch of my sarcasm.

It was a sallow dusk, all the heat sucked out of the air, so I pounded for hours through familiar streets and markets, down near the docks, finally threading my way back along the esplanade, past the Gateway of India. There were three Buddhist monks in a saffron clump asleep under the wall of the Radio Club, guarded by their black umbrellas. I had grown fond of this neighbouring music factory that pumped out ragas day and night, teaching me the rudiments of a rhythmic culture so complex and subtle that I would never manage to do more than acknowledge it. But like the trio of monks, I was lulled by its weaving and patterning. I went inside and smiled good evening to my polite spies, who handed over a key and the information that a gentleman had left a message.

Clutching the envelope and some sorry shreds of hope I ran upstairs and out into the streaky light on my balcony. There were only a few words, in an unfamiliar hand.

> I read the note on your door, inviting one to contact you if one cared to, and hope that you will not mind my presumption in doing so. I am in number twelve, three rooms along, on the same floor. I should be delighted if you were to look me up. Yours respectfully, Alex Carmichael.

Anti-climaxes can induce mild hysteria. I laughed until I thought my brittle racket might wake the monks. Then I walked down the corridor and knocked on Alex Carmichael's door.

He was a perfect gentleman. His brogues were polished so well that they gleamed like the flank of a chestnut thoroughbred. It took us almost an hour of polite manoeuvring to establish that he had been led to believe that because this was India etc I might be accommodating and how stupid of him and he did hope I would excuse his extraordinary lapse and could he please take me to dinner if it were not too late or would I care for a Johnnie

Walker, he had some in his room, awfully easy to get, even in this dry State, if one just knew the right people.

We didn't even drink much of his whisky. We sat on my balcony and talked until the light began to glint again on the morning sea. He was an agent for Lloyds. It mattered to him that my father was a seafarer. I couldn't explain to him why my father had let me come here 'in the circumstances'. I couldn't explain to him that there were always circumstances.

He was leaving in two days. But we were friends. Would I care to come bathing with him after breakfast. He knew a club.

We met out on the esplanade. He had hired a cab. All the bathers were English and drinks were served to them by silent Maharashtrans who wore long starched aprons.

Two months later I received a letter, addressed to me poste restante. Alex was awfully glad we had met, the time we had spent together had been the perfect close to his brief stay in India. It had enabled him to get through what otherwise would have been a rather traumatic time, in the circumstances. And he wanted me to be the first to know that soon after he had arrived home Clare (he had talked about Clare on the balcony) had done him the honour of agreeing to become his wife. He wished me every happiness, and I believed him.

Indira was about to be elected. The monsoon was past. Bul Bul was travelling all around the country and I was going home. He wouldn't accept my sleeping bag as a gift (down was impossible to get in Bombay) so I sold it to him for a risible sum that riled my father years later when I finally told him about it.

The Brick Tower

> The water stood in my eyes to hear this avowal of his dependence: just as if a royal eagle, chained to his perch, should be forced to entreat a sparrow to become its purveyor. But I would not be lachrymose. I dashed off the salt drops, and busied myself with preparing breakfast.
>
> Most of the morning was spent in the open air. I led him out of the wet and wild wood into some cheerful fields: I described to him how brilliantly green they were; how the flowers and hedges looked refreshed; how sparklingly blue was the sky. I sought for him a seat in a hidden and lovely spot; a dry stump of a tree; nor did I refuse to let him, when seated, place me on his knee: why should I when both he and I were happier near than apart? Pilot lay beside us: all was quiet.
>
> *Jane Eyre*

Three months before he died I took him walking. He spared me the ignominy of usurped command by directing everything I did.

'Get the chair with black handles. It steers properly.'

He was right. And this was his old, old pattern: sense and dominance, the canny balance. But I didn't care to argue. He was weighty still and I knew that to push him I needed sound wheels. We watched the cricket together until stumps and then ventured out. He leaned, wincing, on his sticks while I extracted the black handles from the meccano tangle in the hospital storeroom. Walking was his quiet torture. Too many jarring descents into small boats had sent fine fractures all along his shinbones.

'It's warm and light still, Daddy. Let's go right outside.'

We scooted around a long block. It was effortless, downhill. I cantered beside him in the halcyon high humour of a daughter who has got away with something—the slightest misdemeanour, but still something. On the corner of Glen Osmond Road we bogged in the sand of a new street construction. His doctor strode briskly towards us.

'Want a hand Rod? You can't be a light load.'

'No.' I cut him off. 'I'll be fine with him.

We navigate well together. This is just one sticky patch I didn't expect.'

He was a thoughtful doctor and lingered only long enough to satisfy decorum. I heaved and my father shifted in his seat to lend me torque.

'Right hand down,' he instructed. 'Down further. Now straighten up.'

We idled down a side street, past a fantasia garden. It was blotched with petunias and variegated carnations. Scarlet salvia battled puce cinerarias. Dahlias with ingrown talons clung to thin bamboo like the Seventeenth Doll. I bent over and muttered, 'Someone should drive a stake through their hearts and put us all out of our misery.'

The proud gardener caught us staring.

'Would grandfather like to come in and see the flowers up close? This time of year they make such a lovely show. At their very best. Just roll the wheelchair up onto the astroturf and bring the dear old fellow right in.'

We rolled and I exclaimed for him at the raised banks, and the watering system like a nineteenth-century experiment in miniature hydraulics, and the hybridisation. 'Such extraordinary colours,' I said. 'How kind of you to let us see it.'

'Did "grandfather" enjoy that?' I whispered as we escaped.

He grimaced at me, every corner of his face crinkling.

We found ourselves in a dead end, down hill near the olive grove. Over the high wall we could see the top of the brick tower. It was the last standing remnant of the old factory.

'There must have been the right sort of clay around here.'

I was asking him a question, as I always did. But wanted no answer because the disease was in his throat and words came hard.

After a long while he said, very softly, 'It's wonderful, just look at it.'

I traced the painstaking curve and the chequered brick pattern at the top of the tower, a craftsman's flourish.

'That would have been a job of work to send you home happy.'

He nodded. We stayed silent, easy together.

We'd never talked about beauty. That was my mother's province. He had always been utilitarian, protective. When the lilly pilly cracked our driveway he chopped it out and we all called him a vandal. On ships things rust so you maintain them to save your life, he told us. If cracks let in water then you drown. We never really understood his anxiety. We called it obsessiveness. Sometimes it was.

He loathed waste, and made neat hoarders of all of us. But shapeliness left him smiling, and more so when he could fathom a function for it. You'd get no argument if you could show him that the curve or flange was part of the workings. A cello needed its arabesques to shape the sound. He understood that, and would draw diagrams on scrap paper to demonstrate the physics to me. We all saved wads of scrap paper and he would staple them together into telephone pads. He made folders for my mother's music out of stiff old charts and labelled them meticulously on the blank side, using an ebony slide rule that made all his letters flat-bottomed, like pyramids.

I didn't understand where our new conversation, this departure into aesthetics, into simplicity, came from, or why it came, but it seemed natural, even supple. Maybe we had long been rehearsing it, or maybe it was simply too late now for our mute deflections, even for our wits.

We'd been out for more than an hour and his skin was delicate, made fragile by indoors. I turned us around and pushed back up the hill. Heavy going. Halfway there he raised his hand for me to stop. I thought he was resting me. We stood cool under a giant bottlebrush, but he didn't lower his arm. Instead he reached out and with his sheer fingertips drew a laden branch down towards me.

'Look,' he breathed, 'look, how lovely.'

He caught it just long enough for me to see the black points at the ends of fiery stamens. Then he let it go. And as it sprang back the brushes scattered scarlet all over us.

My hands were full with him so I blew it gently out of his hair as I took him home.

Coda: North Country

Where the Northern Ocean, in vast whirls
Boils round the naked melancholy isles
Of farthest Thule: and the Atlantic surge
Pours in among the stormy Hebrides.

I saw the fascination of the locality. I felt the consecration of its loneliness: my eye feasted on the outline of swell and sweep—on the wild colouring communicated to ridge and dell, by moss, by heath-bell, by flower-sprinkled turf, by brilliant bracken, and mellow granite crag.

Jane Eyre

In Bayeux it is so cold at night, even in summer, that you shudder for the men who died nearby in freezing mud, suspended somewhere between earthy hope and seas that drown you decently.

Northern France is patched together only by the relentlessness of grass.

We went to see William's tapestry, the long miracle of linen pieced and sewn by men or women whose fingers understood the heinousness of war even as they embroidered the figures, beheaded them, stripped off their chain mail and left them tumbled in the heraldic borders of the cloth. I carried my granddaughter along its improbable length and showed her the horses that crossed the Channel, and the ships, all stripes and prow, and knights sucked down in the quicksand at Mont Saint Michel. She had only just begun to talk. Horse was fine but quicksand was ambitious. I told her about it anyway and told her how the darning, the feathered herringbone that had kept the tapestry intact for nine hundred years, would have pleased her great-grandfather as much as it pleased his daughter.

He'd been dead for more than four years, but maps, any kind of map—even this stitched chronicle—conjured him so vividly I half expected him to tell me I had taken the wrong turn, or paid too much for a frivolity.

He used to sit sewing canvas, a leather guard on his left hand with an iron disk let in at the base of the thumb and small depressions to catch the thick needle as it pushed through the seams. He made me deck chairs and sheaths for my knives.

We drove south to Chartres. I wondered about history, how this flat country with its long angled perspectives and chiselled trees could ever have conceived an alliance with the drifting shapes of Scotland.

He used to show me his remnants of heritage: a pair of cufflinks with the clan crest on them: three strawberries; *trois fraises*. Fragile, heartshaped woodland fruit. He loved the incongruity of it. So did I.

Chartres juts out of the plain like two shards of bevelled glass. You don't travel to it: it overtakes you. My daughter walked around and around, staring at its façades of angels, saints and demons.

'What kind of religion makes faces so severe? They don't look as though they could imagine heaven.'

We searched for the labyrinth, but there was Mass going on inside so we went out again, out of the murmuring dark, and looked instead at the buttresses and their lavish, slashing energy.

'How did they do it? What kind of nerve must you have to fling stone out at that angle?

How does it work? What on earth possessed them to do it?'

Back home were the books that would explain the mechanics. Maybe the theology as well. We no longer even joked about the reference shelves reduplicted in all our houses, as congenital as freckles.

North-west of Chartres the May countryside grows lush and bountiful. Everything is rounded, the apples, camembert, the demijohns of Calvados. I ate bread on the grass while my children played petanque with silver balls and my grandchild slept in a rug of the wrong tartan. Just wrong enough to smudge the onset of disquieting pastoral.

We reached Mont Saint Michel in time to walk out the long causeway at dusk, a little train of pilgrims with the child hitched to one shoulder or another and the mount changing colour and shedding planes and surfaces in the dying light until it was only a vast silhouette, shaped to a point like the dribbled sandcastles of all our summers.

Next morning it was sharp and faceted, an entire town carved up into the light. My daughter climbed with me. It was Sunday. If you went to High Mass you were allowed up into the Abbey without charge. But the doors were locked behind you and you had to stay the hour. I let the ironies slide into the air and thought only that he would have been amused.

Inside the light was pearly, a green that owed more to seafoam or Persian tiles than to earth and chlorophyll. The lustrous stone pillars seemed to bear no weight at all—as if something else held up the long rectangle of the nave as it flowed unencumbered down to the apse and into sunshine.

But this was still France, where the metaphysics should be seemly. Bells rang, the priest was preceded by a flotilla of close-shaven, cropped Capuchins. They bobbed and knelt in front of us and sang the grand processional with tutored restraint. In my pew I was less tutored and suddenly grateful for the proximity of French and Latin; words slipped onto my keen tongue and music began its undertow of exultation. A psalm, and then the sermon—crisp and Gallic in its intelligence. But more kindly than I could have imagined. And more mysterious. Let it go. Let it go. As the organist began the slow opening pulse of the Sanctus I took my daughter's hand and looked up. In the vault, suspended between two pillars on either side of the altar was a great ship in full sail, tipping lightly on the soundwaves as they swelled and propagated. And high up through the pale glass we caught sight, both of us, of dozens and dozens of gulls as they swooped and wheeled and levelled into formation and then flew out to sea.

CROWN ME WITH
ROSES PASTICHE

JEAN BEDFORD

Jean Bedford was born in England and brought up on the Mornington Peninsula in Victoria. She has been a teacher of English as a Second Language, a journalist and a publisher's editor, as well as a teacher of Creative Writing. She is a novelist and short story writer and her eleventh book, *Now You See Me*, will be published by Random House in 1997. She is married to writer Peter Corris and lives on the Illawarra coast.

There is no possibility of taking a walk on the day the story begins.

The rain sheeted down and the wind howled through the palms outside the house. The long grass among the pecan trees, just glimpsed from my bedroom window, lay flattened and sodden. The mountains in the distance were obliterated by dark, threatening cloud and the track through the property ran like a gleaming river, at least a foot deep.

I sit miserably by my window.

As usual, in this sort of weather, my

cousins had amused themselves by tormenting me and I'd retreated into my own room. Reed never seemed to notice the teasing, although it went on practically under her nose. She wafted about in a haze of sweet-smelling smoke and only intervened when John or Georgie or Beth ran crying to her to complain of something I'd said or done to them. She always believed them—I often heard her telling people her children never told her lies—and she would give an irritable shrug at being roused to do something, and then sit down with me for an exasperated lecture.

I am sly and disruptive.

'You make no effort to fit in here,' she'd say, in her cold, disappointed voice. 'You'd better go to your room and think about things. We all try to accommodate each other here, you know that. You really have to make more effort to live as we do, in peace with each other.'

This life is a lie.

She lived in a dream, Reed, that was not only marijuana induced. Everyone on the property lived in the same dream, as if they'd found a way to go through the looking-glass. If they said a thing was so, then it must be so. They said they lived in peace and harmony with nature, and so the colds and the flu and even occasionally pneumonia, didn't exist. They said their children were happier and freer than those who went to schools and had to obey rules, therefore the bullying and boredom and petulance couldn't be real. They said their love wasn't possessive, and so the jealousy and real hatred among the adults was ignored.

I come from a different world and I pray to go back to it.

Reed scoffed when she caught me on my knees. She told me I'd be better out in the moonlight, opening my arms to the goddess. It was blasphemy: for the first seven years of my life I had been brought up to regular prayers, going to church, a belief in gentle discipline and a good, conventional education.

My parents are dead.

Reed had been married to my mother's brother, and he took me in. Those first few months, when my uncle was still alive, seemed idyllic now, though it had been an unhappy and bewildering time. As soon as he died, Reed sold the house and moved us all up here, buying into this self-contained community. My cousins were delighted—they had been to 'alternative' schools and, as far as I could tell, Reed had never uttered a cross word to any of them. Gateshead Haven was their idea of heaven and their mean natures and uncontrolled selfishness flourished here, among similar children who had never been told 'no' in their lives.

I am out of place at Gateshead.

The other children treated my attempts at politeness with scorn. They assumed my gentle voice and timidity were signs of a poor spirit—like all predators, they recognised their natural victim. And I read books for pleasure. My cousins struggled through the desultory lessons given at apparent random by whatever adult took a fancy to impart some knowledge. Many of the children there could barely read or write, though they all knew every nuance of the television serials.

I couldn't see the pleasure of endless hours sitting in front of a screen, not when there were books that opened worlds of imagination and knowledge.

I am a misfit.

My cousins never let me forget I didn't belong. They were in gangs that terrorised children like me. They shut me up in a dark, cobwebby shed; they pushed me off the steep bank into the dam, although they knew I couldn't swim; they tied me to the railings of the pigpen, with its evil-looking, snorting sow. I learned to avoid them whenever possible, taking long walks, hiding in my room. I also learned not to bother Reed with my 'whining'.

Fortunately Reed had been too lazy, or too uncaring, to get rid of my uncle's books when they moved, and here at Gateshead they were all piled in their cartons, in an unused shed at the back of our house. Books became my retreat, my safe world.

Love is communal.

Lovers were supposed to be communal, but I noticed that Reed's were hers alone while they still interested her. They moved in with us and ignored us until Reed was sick of them.

Many of the children there slept in the kids' compound, since their parents were further along, as Reed put it, on the road to enlightenment, and had relinquished possessiveness even of their offspring. These children were fed and clothed by the community. Some of them didn't know who their parents were and you could see the desperate need to find out in their pinched faces and hungry eyes.

I am neglected, too.

At least I had had real parents, and I could still almost remember them. On a day like this one, the day the story began, I would sit by my window for hours trying to picture my mother. I had photographs, of course, but they seemed of strangers. Mostly, what I could remember was a set of sensations—the smell of her talcum powder, the softness of her breasts, the gentleness of her voice when she knelt beside my bed with me and taught me simple children's prayers.

My father was easier, perhaps because he hadn't been so close. A tall remote man with a deep voice, in my memory he seemed always in silhouette against the open door. I often wondered how my parents would feel, seeing me now. They had named my mother's brother as guardian, but they could never have expected to die so young, or that he would not outlive them long.

I had another aunt, although I'd never met her. She was my father's sister, and she had cut herself off from her family when she married.

'Some weird sect,' Reed would say, when I asked her. 'They live up in the mountains and they believe they'll be the only ones saved on doomsday.'

I dream of being rescued.

I used to think about this other aunt, too, and wonder if she would be kinder than Reed, and if a 'weird sect' in the mountains was any stranger than our lives here at the Gateshead commune. And on the morning I'm talking about, it was almost as if thinking about her conjured her up.

Reed knocked at my door, which was unusual to begin with—she usually left me completely alone unless forced to give me her little lectures.

'Your Aunt Beatie is here to see you,' she said. She looked frightened; something had jolted her out of her normal self-absorbed dream. I leapt off the chair and ran past her.

My prayers are answered.

'Be careful of what you pray for,' goes the proverb, 'because the gods may grant it.' But I didn't know that then. All I knew was that a small, *ordinary* looking woman, neatly dressed and plump, sat in the open hall downstairs, looking disapprovingly at the mess and the high beamed ceilings and the scattered cushions and half-rolled futons. Her gaze seemed to pass over Reed completely when she came in behind me, as if the tousled mane of hair and the beads and the long gauzy skirt, not to mention the nose-rings, were beneath her notice.

Her face sharpened when she saw me properly, however. 'What on earth are you wearing, child?'

We dress like gypsies.

I looked down at myself. I had grown used to the way we dressed—snatching up whatever came to hand from huge piles of unsorted washing that lay about the stair-landing. Now I saw myself through her eyes. I had on an old T-shirt of Reed's and a torn flouncy gypsy skirt. Over them I had draped a crocheted purple shawl and I still wore my yellow rubber boots from before the rain had got so heavy and I had thought of going out to escape my cousins.

'I want to talk to my niece alone,' she said

to Reed, and with an expression of relief, Reed faded out of the room.

'This won't do,' said my aunt. 'You're surely not happy here?'

'No, I hate it,' I said, and burst into tears. I blurted out to her all the things I hated—my cousins' teasing; the bullying from the older children; that there was no proper school. But her interest was properly caught when I had an inspiration and said: 'And Reed won't let me say my prayers properly. She says God doesn't exist, there's only the goddess.'

'It won't do,' she said again. She asked me several questions then, about my belief in God, about sin and redemption, and I answered the way a ten-year-old will who has not really thought much about these things, but trying to convey by my manner an eagerness to be properly taught.

For a while my aunt was silent, then she gave a deep sigh. 'Go back to your room, child,' she said. 'I'd better talk to this Reed person.'

I went back to my room and sat in a frenzy of suppressed excitement.

The thought that I might escape from

Gateshead, from my hateful cousins and my selfish aunt by marriage, whirls in my head like a bright Catherine wheel.

After an hour or so, I was called downstairs again. Reed had packed a bag containing some of the things I'd brought with me, clothes I'd long outgrown. My real aunt, as I thought of her, rejected it with disdain. 'We'll give her what she needs,' she said. She allowed me to bring my photographs of my parents, but not any books. There'd be no need of them, she said, and in my ignorance I assumed that she meant there were plenty of books where we were going.

'Remember,' she said to Reed as we left, 'one word to the proper authorities and I could have this place closed down. Don't ever try to get in touch with Jane again, or I will do it.'

Reed was sullen; she hardly looked at me as I left with my Aunt Beatie. I said a polite goodbye, and made a face at Georgie and Beth, who were staring from the porch. John was nowhere around.

The rain clears as the taxi drives up, and a watery sunlight makes us squint.

I skipped slightly as I went down the track

to the gate and scarcely noticed my Aunt Beatie's firm, restraining hand.

Lowood Retreat was about as far into the mountains as you could go, and then the last few miles were only navigable by water. It was named after the founder of this 'weird sect', Arnold Lowood, a farmer, who had been visited by an angel one day while splitting logs and commanded to sell up all he owned and establish a mission for Christ on earth.

We are very isolated, and contact with the outside world is forbidden.

All our supplies came upriver and were left at the pier, only collected when the delivery man was safely out of sight. I came to realise that my aunt must be a very trusted member of the community to have been allowed to venture out into the world to save my soul.

It had taken her so long to do so because it was years before my parents' solicitors were able to communicate with her. Letters from 'the outside' were ritually burnt on the Friday night bonfires, but *someone* must have read them first, because *someone* had finally summoned her to the Presence.

The Presence had had a vision, Beatie told me with awe in her voice, though later I came to suspect He had found out about the large insurance policy my parents had taken out in my name. But that was much later—I didn't know about it myself, then, nor about Reed's embezzling some of it. At the time I accepted that I had been singled out, somehow, that I was special.

I long to be special, to someone.

What can I tell you about the years at Lowood? Nothing that you could not guess for yourself, especially after the scandal and the revelations of a few years ago, when the road finally went all the way through, and the retreat came under normal scrutiny. The most interesting thing I can tell you is that for a long time I was not aware that I was miserable, even more miserable than I had been at Gateshead. We were told our life was blessed, ordained, that we were privileged above others. And reading the Bible again seemed like a homage to my father's memory.

We dress like Quakers.

We all wore a sort of uniform at Lowood, the females (terms like 'girl' and 'woman' were not used) a sort of shapeless sack, made of thick cotton, that had long sleeves and went from neck to ankles. In winter, which was severe in that altitude, we wore hand-knitted leggings and long-sleeved vests underneath. For some reason we were not allowed to wear gloves, and we all suffered from chilblains. The males wore loose shirts and trousers made of the same coarse cotton—I never found out if they wore woollen underclothes as well against the cold. Looking back, that seems one of the oddest mysteries. The females did all the knitting—yet I never saw anyone make a garment for the males.

The Children of the Blessed Mountain were vegetarians. We ate grains and wizened spinach and watery stews made of parsnip and lentils. There was no television.

There are no books except the New Testament.

It was rumoured among the children that the Presence owned a radio, but since we never saw Him, let alone went near his private rooms, we never knew.

My Aunt Beatie changed almost as soon as

we entered the grounds. She put away the tweed suit and the ordinary shoes and donned one of the sacks. She took her hair out of its rather becoming bun and scratched it back harshly from her face with a headband that seemed made of steel. She showed me to the female children's dormitory and then went away. I didn't see her for several days, and when I did, she told me curtly she had been fasting and praying to cleanse herself of her contact with the ungodly.

Again, we had no school, or not as I imagined school to be.

We spend hours at Bible Study and in learning by heart verses from Revelations.

Our days were taken up by helping in the vegetable gardens or minding the babies. Every evening one of us would have to recite the verses we had learned that day, before we sat down to our early and sparse meal. In recitation I excelled, and it gave me pleasure. With nothing else to read, I pored over the Bible, and I found it easy to memorise the passages.

My aunt warns me against the sin of pride.

I learned to conceal my enthusiasm.

By seven o'clock we were in our beds and the lights were out. We were all so cowed that there were never even the slightest whispers after curfew, though the sound of suppressed sobbing could sometimes be heard. What the adults did at night I didn't know, then, but the newspaper revelations since have given me some idea. Sex was so frowned upon, officially, that it still seems incredible. We young ones were segregated for everything except Bible Study, and even then the young females sat at one side of the room and the young males at the other.

I hardly ever saw my aunt. In fact, I realised slowly, I had been placed in the same position as the parentless kids at the commune. All the children at the retreat were separated from their families at the age of six and put into the dormitories. You could tell which girls had had unorthodoxly affectionate parents from the strength and duration of their night-time weeping. By looking carefully around at group prayers you could make a guess at which were their mothers and fathers—the males and females with the red eyes and the determined ignoring of the pleading faces in the children's section.

In short, it was hell, though we were smugly persuaded it was heaven on earth and gave daily thanksgiving for our privilege. I had one friend, and that made it all worthwhile.

I have never had a friend before.

Her name was Helen, and she was always in trouble for one thing or another. She was genuinely pious; her transgressions troubled her. But, however hard she tried, she couldn't suppress her natural spirits, her energy and excitement.

Constantly, Helen was called out to the front at the Saturday Meetings, and chastised for her nonconformity. I used to cringe for her, dreading a day when I might be singled out in the same way, but she bounced back, always. I came across her once, standing in a corner, balanced uncomfortably one-legged on a rickety stool. She had her eyes closed and was reciting the book of Luke.

I look around quickly to make sure no one is about, and then I whisper to her:

'Helen, there's no one here. You can stop now.'

Barely pausing in her recitation she said, 'No, I can't stop. It's my punishment and it's right and just. I *must* try to be good.'

Later, in bed, she was whimpering with

cramp, but she made me promise not to call anyone to help. Much later still, after a day tied to the tankstand in icy winds, she caught pneumonia and after that she died. The Children did not believe in doctors or conventional medicine, and they gave her minimal treatment.

But for several years we were happy in each other's company. Her parents had come late to the retreat and she had known a different life before. We shared stories out of books we had read, and we shared dreams of escape—or, at least, I shared mine. Reed had had some effect on me after all—I was a secret rebel under all my outward pious conformity. Helen seemed to have no wish to leave the place, only to make herself more worthy of it. It was one of my many disillusionments with Lowood—that she, who was more genuinely humble than almost anyone else, was so little valued by anybody there.

But there were times, very few, when we could evade the overlooking eyes of the adults, and then we would walk together through a forest track to where the river dammed slightly on an outcrop of rocks, forming a shingly beach.

We sit on an old log and throw stones and sticks into the brown swirling water, and tell each other stories in which we are the heroines.

Helen's dreams were mostly about being admitted into the Presence. Mine were about a life after this, a life of study and ordinary pursuits, of love and happiness. But I couldn't see how to bring it about.

In my eagerness to please, not to be singled out for punishment, I have succeeded too well.

In one of my rare encounters with my aunt she told me grimly that 'they' were pleased with my progress; that I was being marked for higher service. Even then, this filled me with anxiety. There were young females, I knew, called Acolytes, who lived in the Presence's house, who served Him and didn't mix with the rest of us. They were extolled in the group meetings as blessed above all other females, but I noticed, with my sharp, secret eye, that when they appeared at the monthly thanksgiving rites they looked more bowed down and confused than transfigured with heavenly joy.

I was sixteen when I had that conversation with my aunt. I realised that at eighteen I might be inducted into the Acolytes. I spoke about it to Helen, who was already sick with her last illness, but she was no help. Her admiration and guileless envy made her breathless, and she spoke between coughs, 'Oh, Jane, you are so lucky. I would die happy if I thought I would be allowed to live with the Presence and serve Him.'

She did die happy. I was told the Presence Himself came to her deathbed and held her hand for the last minutes of her life. They wouldn't let me in to visit her then, but I was allowed to view the body, decked out in soft white linen of a finer quality than any of us usually saw.

I fall on her corpse, sobbing, and I am led away to the punishment chapel to say prayers for hours on my knees.

I missed the funeral and a rare chance to see the Presence in person.

I was seventeen by then. There were three of us, young females of the same age, and we were removed from the general run of things at about the same time. We were taken to a small building set apart from the main compound, and for three months we didn't leave it, except for supervised exercise when the others were at evening meals. We were allowed to grow our hair long, for the first time, and we were given dresses to wear of snowy white cotton, with coloured ribbons around the waist. My ribbon was blue; Naomi's was green and Hester's was red. We were excused from our usual chores, though we still had two hours of Bible Study each morning with one of the older females.

Suddenly we were treated with deference, smiled at and cosseted. We were told how pretty we were, how valuable to the Children for our youth and our virtue. Of course, we blossomed under the attention. We were allowed mirrors for the first time, and not chastised for vanity when we looked into them.

Sometimes we were taken to a sort of long gallery where there were cushions and couches, and told to sit there for a while, reading our Bibles.

We know we are being watched by someone, perhaps the Presence Himself, and we preen and show off.

I was the only one who had any anxiety—the other two laughed at me. 'The Acolytes live a pretty easy life,' Naomi said. 'They don't have to cook or work in the gardens, and they get better food, too.'

'But they must have to do something to earn it,' I said. 'And they don't look happy.'

'Rubbish,' Hester said. 'They're serving the Presence—they *must* be happy.'

Now, of course, the whole world knows why they were unhappy, the perversions they learned and the humiliations they suffered until they got too old (in their early twenties), or got pregnant, and were cast off into the general community to be shared by the other males. None of us three could have guessed at that, but still I was uneasy.

Yet, if fate hadn't intervened again, I might have accepted everything, as the others did. And again, fate came in the shape of an aunt, this time one I'd never heard of. In fact, she was a great-aunt, the sister of my maternal grand-mother, and she had been living abroad for many years. She'd traced me through a private detective, having only recently learned of her niece's death, and she appeared at Lowood like a fairy godmother.

She was accompanied by the same private detective (a huge, brawny ex-policeman) and they'd hired a boat to get up the river. It seemed to me they broke through the community like a storm, leaving gasping members in their wake.

Stews burn on the stove, spades lie in the furrows, children run unattended in the crèche, while adult males and females run to keep up with this tiny juggernaut and her henchman.

She burst in on our Bible lesson, a wave of French perfume seeming to precede her. 'Mon Dieu, what is this?' she cried. 'Which of you is Jane? It must be you, my dear,' she came to me immediately. 'You're so pretty—just like your mother.' I loved her from that moment.

She was dressed in her idea of what a lady wore on a boating trip—khaki shirt, loose slacks, ropy espadrilles. To me, she looked stylish and sophisticated.

'Ghastly frock,' was her next comment. 'The sooner we get you out of this, the better. Who's the boss?'

My Aunt Beatie came running up, red in the face. She had got fat in the years I was there. 'I'm her legal guardian,' she said, panting.

Great-aunt Fairfax gave her a cool stare. 'No,' she said slowly, 'I don't think you are, actually.'

She turned to me. 'Are you sixteen yet, child?'

I am overcome by her presence, but I already know I will go anywhere she will take me.

'I'm seventeen, nearly eighteen,' I managed to say.

'Then you are legally independent. All you have to do is decide where you want to be. Do you want to come with me, or stay here . . .' she looked around at the poorly constructed room, the drab people, 'with them?'

'With you.' I could hardly get the words out. *Cinderella* had been one of my favourite stories, I now remembered.

'But you have been Chosen,' my Aunt Beatie cried out. 'You will be an Acolyte.'

'Good God, woman, what century are you living in?' My great-aunt gave a surprisingly hearty laugh for such a small woman. 'If you come with me, Jane, you can be anything you want to be, but I doubt if you'll choose to be anyone's acolyte.'

I was already moving towards her and the comforting bulk of her companion. 'I'm coming with you,' I said, my voice surprising me with its confidence. 'I'm coming with you now.'

We were halfway there before I even thought to ask *where* we were going. The boat, then a hired car, then a plane. A train and another plane; cities I'd barely heard of, people dressed in ways

I'd forgotten; women like my great-aunt, in swirls of makeup and perfume, men in jeans or suits. There was a brief rush around a department store in Sydney, to buy me a few necessities, as she called them: luxuries I didn't even know existed—delicate lace underwear, soft skirts, shoes of supple leather, silk blouses and cambric shirts.

'You *must* be the fairy godmother,' I breathed once, and she gave her hearty laugh again.

'Baby, I was nominally your mother's godmother, but I failed her dismally when she really needed me. Now I'm going to make it up. To you.'

Finally I did ask. 'Where are we going?'

I expected, wanted the laugh, and I got it.

'To the back of beyond, unfortunately. For the present, anyway.'

The back of beyond was a sheep station, somewhere in north-western New South Wales, where she worked: 'Again, nominally,' she laughed, as a companion to the owner's sister, who was 'delicate'. In fact, Bertha Rochester was another relative of hers—'On my husband's side, darling, nothing to do with you.' I didn't notice, then, the slightly emphasised reassurance in what she said. I hardly noticed anything, except that she called me *darling*, and was continually patting me and hugging me and stroking back my hair.

I bask in the attentions I have hardly known I missed.

Did my heart drop when I realised that Thornfield Station was almost as remote from the world as Lowood? I don't remember now, since it so quickly became the centre of my universe, the place where all comfort and happiness resided.

There were no neighbours within fifty kilometres, and most of that intervening land belonged to Thornfield. The run was unimaginably huge, the size of a small European principality. The stockmen had cottages scattered about, very distant from the main house, and some of them had wives and children but I didn't meet them at first.

Thornfield station-house was a large, verandahed one-storey place, surrounded by gardens kept moist from their own bore-holes.

Past the gardens, the eroded, over-cropped and parched land stretched in every direction as far as the horizon. But roses grew in a huge bed in front of the house, blowsy and perfumed, and honeysuckle climbed sweetly over the verandah rails. I picked a sprig as I entered the house. Smelling it seemed to renew my optimism.

It was nearly dark, and the place felt deserted; there were no lights on that I could see. Our driver, a taciturn man called Jake, had left us at the steps and driven off.

I turn to watch his dust trail shimmering in the last purple rays of the dying sun, until he disappears in the gathering shadows.

I stood by the door, looking uncertainly at my great-aunt.

She rummaged around in her oversized bag and finally produced a keyring. She unlocked the heavy door and stood back dramatically for me to enter first. Over my shoulder she pressed a switch and a mellow light came on. The wide hallway seemed to bisect the house, and the soft gleam of polished furniture reflected the last of the dusk through a huge window at the far, unlighted end.

Many rooms seemed to open off the passage and I hesitated, waiting for my great-aunt to show me where to go.

'Your room, first, I think,' she said and gestured to a door on my right. 'It's nothing much.' She opened the door and again let me enter first.

'I'm next door, after the bathroom, which we share. I'll let you get settled, my love. Then come to the kitchen—the door opposite this one—and we'll scramble up something to eat.'

She shut the door behind her and I sat on the bed and surveyed my new home. There was a desk and a chair, a built-in wardrobe, a small two-seater couch and a television on a wheeled cabinet. I got up and opened the door in the far wall. It led to a bathroom, a magnificent one in my view. A huge sunken bath, fluffy towels on a heated rail, a toilet behind a glass screen. While I gazed, the door in the opposite wall opened and my great-aunt poked her head in. 'You can have a bath if you want,' she said. 'There's plenty of water at the moment. Floods, you know.' She popped back out again like a jack-in-the-box.

To me Thornfield seems like heaven.

I was too tired and hungry then, but I promised myself a long soak before I went to bed. At Lowood we had rostered weekly baths in the communal wash-house, with one of the older females keeping watch over us to make sure we didn't add to the carefully measured three inches of tepid liquid we were allowed. As trainee Acolytes, Hester and Naomi and I had been allowed a daily bath, but we shared the water.

I splashed myself with warm water and buried my face in the thick towel, which smelled faintly of lavender.

Although I feel guilty that such earthly luxuries should matter so much, I am nearly weeping with pleasure and gratitude.

I wondered then how long it would be before the strictures of Lowood would fade from my conscience. The answer was, of course, never, but I was blissfully unaware of that.

For the next few days I helped Aunt Fairfax—she hated her first name, Agatha—in her apparently very light duties around the house.

The family was away staying with friends in Sydney, and when they came back, several of the stockmen's wives would come up to the house to do the cooking and heavy work. She checked linen closets, made lists of things that we needed to restock the larder and the giant freezer, pottered in the garden and arranged the overblown roses in crystal vases.

Their petals drop and lie reflected on rich polished wood.

She was a sort of superior housekeeper, I realised, as well as companion to Bertha Rochester. I tried to find out as much as I could about the Rochesters, but my aunt was blithely uninformative. There was a little girl in the household, too, she said, Adele, who was a darling, though sometimes uncontrolled. Mr Rochester was her guardian, and he himself was seldom at the house—he was usually out about the property, working with the stockmen and staying in one of the many shacks. Or he was in New Zealand, skiing, or in Malaysia, where he had unspecified business interests.

He is a reticent man of great charm, my aunt says with an air of finality, as if that is all there is to say about him.

'And his sister?' I asked. 'What's she like?'

She looked at me, oddly, I thought. 'She has her moments,' she said finally, in her dry light voice. 'You'll make up your own mind, no doubt.' But I thought there was some shadow of worry in her face and I began to feel the first slight apprehension.

I had realised by now that my first entry to the house had been through the back door. There was another road into the property, ending in a splendid gravelled driveway at the other side of the house. There was also a swinging door in the hall which closed off the family's quarters from ours. While they were away my aunt had it propped open. When they were in residence we were expected to keep to our part of the house. It rankled somewhat, as if we were servants, but I didn't really mind. I was living in more comfort than I could have imagined and so far had virtually nothing to do. I wondered if they would find a task for me, or whether they would simply tolerate me as a hanger-on of my aunt's.

'Well,' she said, when I asked her about it, 'I had thought that you might act as a sort of governess to Adele—her nurse is French and she has not managed to learn much English yet. But I don't know.' She looked at me doubtfully. 'You only seem to have studied the Bible at that place. I don't suppose you speak any French?'

I shook my head. 'But she and I could teach each other,' I said. 'That way it will seem like a game and she might be more interested.'

My great-aunt looked pleased at the thought. I wondered if she, too, had been anxious about my place there. I still couldn't quite work out her own role. I assumed the Rochesters paid her a wage, yet she had said that Bertha was a family connection. I didn't know her well enough, I thought, to ask direct personal questions about her circumstances, and for such a talkative woman, she was still extremely tactful when discussing anything to do with the family at Thornfield. I bided my time—no doubt things would become clearer in a few days when the Rochesters came home.

I spend hours each day wandering in the garden, finding places to sit on stone benches beside pools filled with koi and carp and yellow waterlilies.

The seasons didn't seem to matter at Thornfield; winter jasmine blossomed at the same time as summer flowers, and the roses seemed always to be laden with blooms.

Sometimes I sat in the 'library', really Edward Rochester's study, but he never used it as such. It was a shadowy, polished room, lined with bookshelves, filled with books. I lost myself there, in a trance of pleasure, among novels I'd never heard of, biographies of people I never knew existed. Aunt Fairfax said that no one would mind if I took away books to my own room, but I didn't quite dare. Being allowed to read them at all filled me with a sort of delighted guilt. I always felt that one of the Children of the Blessed Mountain might appear at any moment and snatch away the profane and delicious volumes.

I sit, curled up on the window seat, several books always piled around me.

I never knew what to read first; I could never choose just one, I always took down three or four, just so I knew they were there, to hand. And I was sitting there when I first met Edward Rochester.

'Who the hell are you?' These were the first words he ever spoke to me and they startled me, almost as if one of the adult males from the retreat had indeed, found out my crime.

'Oh,' he turned away and ran his fingers through his thick, dark hair. 'I remember, you're Mrs F's niece.'

I stood up, trembling. 'I'm sorry. My great-aunt said it would be all right if I read in here . . .'

'What?' He turned back towards me. 'Yes, of course it's all right. No one else ever uses the room.' He stared at me, and at the books piled around me and he gave a slight grin, just a quirk to his mouth, but I couldn't tell if it was sarcastic or approving. He wrenched open the door behind him and yelled into the passage. 'Bertha. Come here a minute. Meet our new guest.'

The woman who appears a few moments later is immediately, instinctively, my enemy, and she knows it—though at first she pretends I am too insignificant for such a strong word.

She greeted me politely enough, but I felt her weighing me up and deciding against me, implacably. She was a tall, spare woman, with dark skin and eyes and thick wavy hair pulled back into a long ponytail. She had a slight resemblance only to her brother. She was dressed with a casual elegance that suddenly made me feel that my new jeans were too baggy, my shirt too neatly tucked in.

With jerky, fluttering gestures, that I was to realise were habitual to her, she turned to her brother and began speaking about people I didn't know. I felt a dull angry hotness spread into my cheeks. She'd dismissed me as of no account within minutes of seeing me. I stood, awkwardly, not knowing whether to push past them and back to my own part of the house, or to sit down again on my window seat. Bertha solved the problem for me by taking Mr Rochester's arm and leading him from the room, still chattering about a woman called Blanche who was coming to stay with her. Neither of them said goodbye.

I stand until I feel my cheeks return to their normal pallor, then carefully collect up the books and put them back in the shelves.

I couldn't find my great-aunt anywhere, and assumed she was with Bertha. Then I heard a child's voice from the garden, chattering shrilly, with a more measured woman's voice answering her. It must be Adele with her nanny. I hesitated at the door. What if they were as rude as the Rochesters? Still, I would have to meet them, if

I was to earn my keep trying to teach the little girl.

I found them at the old swing under a giant chestnut tree at the bottom of the garden. Adele sat grasping the ropes, while her nurse pushed her vigorously. When they saw me they stopped their chatter and the nanny began to still the swing. 'Bon jour,' I said slowly—my great-aunt had taught me this—'je m'appelle Jane.'

Adele tried it and giggled. 'Zhaeene,' she managed, nearly falling off the swing in her amusement. She was a startlingly pretty child, with flaxen hair and perfect white skin. I wondered how they kept her from freckling in this climate, then noticed the old-fashioned straw hat lying on the grass. She was about seven, then, poor little Adele, an uncomplicated, undisciplined child, and God knows what has become of her now.

Her nurse, Sophie, was pleasant enough, and also uncomplicated. Her face fell when she realised I had exhausted all my French. Her English was poor. But we managed for the first few weeks to communicate by sign-language and pointing, and a lot of laughter. Eventually her

English became quite good—much better than my French, which is still primitive.

If it had only been them and my aunt I had to deal with, I would have been happy from the beginning at Thornfield, but Bertha Rochester was there, too, a constant sardonic presence. Her eyebrow lifted when she noticed I had taken in my jeans and wore my shirt loose now, and she said something under her breath to her friend Blanche Ingram, who had arrived from her nearby station. They both laughed, then ignored me pointedly for the rest of Blanche's visit.

Edward Rochester I scarcely saw. As my aunt had said, when he was at Thornfield he stayed well away from the house—and, I couldn't help wondering—from his sister, too? When I did see them together I was baffled at their relationship. She teased him sharply, and seemed always to be watching him. He treated her with a sort of edgy tolerance, never biting back at her enigmatic taunts, but excusing himself as soon as he could from her company.

Once I catch him staring at her when she isn't looking, and it seems to me there is something brooding and inimical in his eyes. I think:

he stays away from her as much as he can. He hates her, too.

But after the first few weeks, I got used to things and life became easier. Adele turned out to have a sweet nature under her spoilt airs and she began to regard me with a satisfying affection, trying to please me as much as she could, diligently practising her English on anyone who came near and pretending to teach the cat the language if she could find no one else to listen. Bertha went away for an unspecified time, on a return visit to her friend Blanche's place, and the house was virtually left to my aunt and Sophie and myself to run. I began to use the library again, and even to take books away to read at night. I wondered if Edward Rochester would appear more frequently now that his sister had gone, and to my pleasure—which surprised me—he did.

Sometimes he would come out to the verandah where I sat with Adele and Sophie while we laughingly tried to absorb each other's language. I had found an old blackboard in one of the sheds and had set up my idea of a schoolroom—the schoolroom I had always wanted. We would take it in turns, the three of us, to play teacher, drawing rough approximations of objects, then writing the French and English words beside them. Some mornings we spoke only in French (which meant I hardly spoke at all), but mostly we spoke English, as it was more important for them to acquire the new language.

At first we were shy in his presence, except that Adele would begin to show off to catch his attention, but after a time we took it for granted and went back to our old enjoyment of the 'lessons'. He would turn over the pages of a book or a magazine, apparently not listening, but every now and then I would see him smile at one of Adele's more charming faux pas.

My heart lifts when he smiles. His dark, usually grave face lights up then and he seems a younger, happier man, as if he sheds a lifetime of disappointment. I come to live for these smiles. I wait every morning for his appearance, his soft apology for disturbing us, and if he doesn't come I feel bereft.

I thought he was lonely and shy, that he needed kindness and understanding, so that he would smile more often. But I was too shy myself to initiate anything.

I felt almost from the beginning that I loved

him. I was not quite eighteen, remember, and I had hardly met a man before, certainly not an attractive one. At Lowood we had very little contact with the adult males, and with their identical uniforms of denim and their plain serious faces, there had been none who ever struck me as a man, as such. I was beginning to have fantasies about Edward Rochester, as girls do, even though he was so much older than me. And I was beginning to hope that he liked me, too, unsophisticated child that I was. But our fantasies don't take account of the commonsense realities. We build ideals of love and we dream dreams in which the object of our adoration conforms to these ideals.

I hardly know him, but I am deeply in love with him before he even notices me.

In fact, underneath everything—and I scarcely knew what that everything consisted of—he was a kind man. He wasn't shy, as I imagined, but he'd become reclusive. He told me this as we gradually became friends of a sort. He would stop me as I went to return a book to its place on the shelves, and ask me about it. He invited me to listen to music with him after dinner, which he now ate with my great-aunt and Sophie and me. He told me stories about his travels all over the world, adventures, like the ones Othello told to Desdemona (I was working my way through the *Collected Plays of Shakespeare*). He was cultured and widely read and his conversation enthralled me. He must have been aware of my infatuation, and I think it touched him and amused him, too.

But then Bertha comes back. She is nervy and restless and she soon drives him out of the house again.

My aunt went about with a worried look, and I saw her several times go to Bertha's room late at night, carrying what looked like tablets and a glass of water on a tray.

On one of Edward's rare visits I heard fragments of a conversation my aunt had with him, before she closed the kitchen door. '. . . Grace, again, perhaps?' I heard, then his swift, angry reply. 'No. Not that woman. Not yet. We'll . . .'

The next day he left in the four-wheel-drive, without saying goodbye.

I wave from the verandah, so does Adele, but he doesn't turn his head.

My aunt was vague about where he had

gone—business in Sydney, she thought.

'How long will he be away?' I asked.

'I don't know, child.' She looked at me hard. 'A while, I hope.'

For the next few days strong winds flew up out of the plains, swirling and lifting dust-devils off the paddocks, coating the place in gritty red sand. The roses were battered and torn and the heavy air inside the house felt full of electricity. My aunt developed a harsh, dry cough—she had not been well for some time, and she seemed to have grown frail suddenly, losing all the nervous charm and vitality that had so attracted me at first. She also began to talk about me going to Sydney, to do some study of some sort. As she said, my education had been woefully neglected. I would have money when I turned eighteen, she told me, and explained about my parents' insurance.

'There's not as much as there should be,' she said, 'but enough for you to be independent.' Then she told me how Reed had inveigled large sums from the trustees for my 'upkeep', though she had spent it on establishing herself comfortably at the commune. 'You could probably sue her, if you wanted,' she said. But I didn't care.

Reed seemed like a stranger from another world, a character in a book, perhaps, and I no longer wished her harm.

I no longer wished to go to Sydney, either, or to have an independent life. I said I might do some subjects by correspondence, as Adele had begun to do under my supervision now that her English was adequate. Perhaps I'd think about it later, I said, and my aunt sighed.

'I've let you down,' she said. 'I should have taken you straight to Sydney and got you into a good boarding school. But I was lonely, my dear. I'm just a selfish old woman, I'm afraid. I wanted someone of my own to love for a while.'

I understood that, and I felt a wave of affection for her.

But I hug to myself the fantasy of Edward, that he might begin to love me, that all my future happiness lies in this place, with this man.

My aunt sensed how I felt and I could see it worried her, but she had lost the energy to impose herself on the situation.

For the first few days Edward was away, Bertha hardly came out of her room. She seemed to be sleeping most of the time and I wondered if she was ill. Then one morning I heard her voice, raised sharply, shouting at my aunt. I went to my window and looked out. Jake stood by the four-wheel-drive, with Bertha's luggage piled in the back. He stared off into the distance, waiting to see who would win the argument.

'You can't go, Bertha,' my aunt said anxiously, coughing, bending under the malicious, grit-laden wind. 'You're not well, my dear.'

'Shut up. I know what you've been doing, you old cow. Well I fooled you. I didn't take them last night, or this morning, and I'm going. You can't stop me.' She flung herself into the jeep and Jake drove off. My aunt turned back towards the house with an expression of, I thought, exaggerated despair. Why shouldn't Bertha do as she liked and go wherever she wanted? But I knew if I asked my aunt about it I would get another of her infuriatingly vague answers.

However, I was tired of things being kept from me, and I stood in my doorway and listened as she dialled a number on the hall phone. I knew she was calling Edward, though I still found her end of the conversation puzzling.

'Oh, you're still there,' my aunt said with

relief. 'Have you? ... Oh, well, she's on her way there. I couldn't stop her, I'm sorry ... Yes, perhaps it's just as well ... But I really do think Grace ... It's up to you, of course, but it's harder now I'm getting old ... All right. Yes. Goodbye.' She stood with her hand on the phone for a few moments, then walked tiredly past me to her room without seeing me. I thought I heard a faint sob before she closed her door.

I couldn't work it out and after a while I shrugged and went to find Adele.

I wonder if Edward will come home now.

He did come home several days later and for a while I was completely happy. The wind storms were over, and in their aftermath the air seemed washed and sweet. My aunt pruned back the tattered rose bushes and we settled into a routine at Thornfield that was comfortable and serene. Both Adele and I did lessons by correspondence, helping each other with arithmetic, which I couldn't see the point of. But I read everything there was to read in the library and educated myself that way. I wanted to be educated for Edward—not for myself, but so that he would find me interesting to talk to. I had completely lost sight of my old ambitions to do something in the world—I was focused solely on love and happiness. And that happiness centred on Edward.

I am living in a sort of dream world of my own making, fed on romances I read, and on the slightly unreal quality of life so isolated and confined.

All my aunt said about Bertha's absence was that she'd decided to stay on in Sydney with friends. I let it pass. I didn't care where she was, as long as she wasn't at Thornfield. With her gone Edward came back to the house, joining us in the evenings after his long days out with the stockmen or after working in his office by the stables. He even seemed less irritated by Adele's prattle, and let her sometimes sit on his knee, though he would sharply gesture to Sophie to take her to bed if she got too demanding. I felt sorry for the child then, as she obviously adored him and was basking in his new indulgence. I started to feel that I might be in the same situation, mistaking his courtesy and occasional attention for something deeper, and so I began to take special care never to impose my company on him unless he specifically invited it.

I liked to take long walks in these balmy evenings, after dinner, through the garden and out into the paddocks which seemed so hostile in the glare of the sun. At night, bathed in moon-light, it was a magical landscape, and no matter how long I walked in any direction I could always see the comforting lights of the house to guide me back.

One night, as if by accident, I meet Edward having one of his rare cigarettes under the old magnolia tree, which is always in bud or flow-ering, drenching the night with its strong perfume.

'You're avoiding me, Janie,' he said. 'So this is where you disappear to at night when you don't want my company.'

'Oh no, I'm not,' I stammered. 'I do want your company, only . . .' I trailed off, miserably embarrassed.

He laughed and began to walk with me. After that, with nothing being arranged, it became a habit, and he waited for me every night on the verandah.

My days now are spent in even more of a dream, waiting for the evening, waiting to be alone with him under the bright stars.

I knew in my bones, as you do know these things, that he was beginning to feel what I wanted him to feel for me. Aunt Fairfax watched and looked anxious, but didn't say anything to me. She went to bed very early these nights, soon after Adele, and I think she was already deciding that she only had energy enough for herself. Rescuing me from the retreat had been her last adventure.

Edward and I grew close on these walks, our conversation ranging over everything and anything, with me pouring out my meagre life history to him one night, or listening to his plans for the station on another.

Almost imperceptibly we grew physically intimate as well. At first there was the occasional hand on my elbow when I stumbled over a tussock or a buried root, which somehow became a natural holding of hands. I hardly noticed the night he began to walk with his arm around my shoulders. It might have been intended as nothing more than a sort of neutral, avuncular affection, but I nestled in under his arm in a way that was not niece-like. He didn't say anything to stop me, and one night, finally, he turned my face up to his after I had said something naive that amused him, and kissed me, lightly on the lips. Then he held me at arms' length and stared at me.

I move, almost in a faint, towards the next kiss, which is not light. Then he almost shoves me away from him.

'You're too young,' he said. 'I can't take advantage of you like this.'

'I don't care,' I said. 'I love you with all my heart.'

'Yes,' he said, almost sadly, 'I believe you do. But you have no one to compare me with. If you had any real guardians, apart from a tired old woman, they would warn you against me, Jane.' He moved away, towards the house, and muttered, 'And rightly so, too. Come on, let's go back.'

We walked back in silence, and his familiar enclosing arm remained by his side. I felt panic—had I offended him by my youth and awkwardness, my blurting out those words of commitment? From being my closest companion, he had suddenly become an intimidating stranger. I was too confused to find any words to speak to him.

He left me abruptly at the house, where I stood for a while staring at the thorny sticks of the denuded roses. Then I went to bed, where I tossed and turned into the small hours.

When I finally sleep, I dream of a wedding and that I am crowned with yellow rosebuds. I wait at the altar and no bridegroom appears. There are no guests, no minister. The church is a ruin and howling winds blow my lace veil away, with the roses. The dream dissolves into meaningless, half-heard conversation in French. I wake with tears running down my face.

The next morning he had gone, to collect Bertha from the Ingrams', my aunt said, and perhaps to stay there a while himself. I hadn't known that Bertha was on her way back. Edward never talked about her, never mentioned her name, and I had had no urge to remind him of her. My aunt peered at my heartbroken face and said, 'It's for the best, Jane. He's not for you. You should think again about going to Sydney, meeting some young people, making yourself a life.'

I had no wish for any life that didn't include Edward Rochester, and now I felt I had destroyed my chance of that through my own clumsiness.

In those next few weeks, my future, which has seemed to open and flower in front of me, becomes as bare and thorny as the poor rose trees.

I stumbled through the days, going over and over our last few words, wishing I had said something different, something that would have held him to me. I thought I would never be more miserable, but I was wrong. Bertha returned home without him and my life became a living hell.

My aunt looked appalled when she saw Bertha get out of the jeep alone. She knew she was coming—we had arranged for her rooms to be cleaned and I had even picked fresh flowers to put beside her bed—but my aunt had obviously expected someone else as well.

'Where is Grace?' she asked, as Bertha came into the house, Jake following with her cases.

'I sent her away,' Bertha said, with a malicious grin. 'Where you and Edward will never find her. I've given her money to stay hidden, this time. And I'll do the same to anyone else you try to bring in her place.'

'Does Edward know?' I couldn't understand why my aunt was so upset.

'No. He's gone off on his travels thinking

I'm safely imprisoned here with my gaolers.' She gave a wild laugh and moved past us to her part of the house. I heard the first few bars of a loud recorded symphony coming from the living-room before she slammed the door shut. Jake left, as usual, without speaking.

All I could think of was that Edward had gone away somewhere without telling me. He never wanted to see me again, that was clear. He was expecting me to leave Thornfield and be gone when he got back. Perhaps he had even told my aunt to persuade me to go. Well, I would go, I decided. As soon as I turned eighteen, in a few weeks, I would take my inheritance and leave.

My heart turns to stone at the thought.

But meanwhile there were the days to get through. Bertha's behaviour had become deeply strange. Her sudden, fluttering gestures seemed almost frenetic now, and she had moods of dreadful hilarity, rushing through the house, ordering horses to be saddled, galloping off across the downs for hours. Once she insisted that I ride with her, then tried to goad me further than my novice's careful canter. When we were miles from the house she slapped my pony's rump and laughed loudly and cruelly when he bolted and I was thrown into stinging shrubs. She rode off, still laughing, leaving me to catch the snorting beast and limp my way back. She didn't even stay to make sure I had no bones broken. When I had my bath that night I realised I was bruised all over.

At other times she withdrew into a sullen, brooding silence. She would speak to no one for days on end, but sit glaring into space, crooning a tuneless song to herself, snarling at anyone who went near her. Or she would silently follow us around as we went through our daily routines, making us all uneasy. There was malice in her and she cast a sort of shadow of it around her in these moods. Even Adele was subdued by it, keeping close to me or Sophie, talking in a low murmur instead of her usual, high-pitched excited voice. Sophie told me that Bertha often slapped the child, if she thought no one was watching, though she always denied it when Adele ran crying for comfort. 'But the little one does not lie,' Sophie said to me. 'She is bad, that other one.'

I believed her. I thought there was evil in Bertha, and obvious madness. Even when she appeared to be friendly, there was some mockery, some sadistic amusement in her face. Finally, one day when she had tormented me to tears again, I insisted on Aunt Fairfax talking to me honestly about it. At first she tried to be evasive, as usual.

'Just try to avoid her, if you can,' she said.

'I think she's mad,' I said. 'I'm afraid of her.' And I was.

She follows me on my evening walks, keeping to the shadows. I hear her hoarse breathing, and once a weird, echoing laugh.

I had begun staying inside at night, and then I would hear her pacing up and down the hall outside my room. I heard her stop in front of my door several times, but when I opened it there would be no one there, just the middle door swinging on its hinges.

My great-aunt looked alarmed when I told her all this. 'You must lock your door,' she said. 'Bertha will calm down. These phases never last very long, any more.' But her voice was uncertain.

'What phases?' I said. 'You have to be honest with me, for once. There's something badly wrong here, something about Bertha. You have to tell me.'

'Oh God,' she said, and sat down by the kitchen table. 'I promised Edward not to say anything. But he stays away, and I'm too old to cope any more . . .'

'Cope with what?' I sat down opposite her, not caring if I upset her, only determined to find out what was going on.

She gave a shaky sigh which turned into one of her racking coughs, then apparently made up her mind. 'Bertha has always been . . . difficult,' she said. 'I used to help look after her at first, with Grace Poole, who was a trained nurse. Then she seemed so much better for a while, and Edward brought her home and asked if I would come just to keep an eye on her when he wasn't here.'

'Difficult how?' I persevered. I sensed that she would tell me everything now. 'What was she like before?'

'Wild,' she said, and sighed again. 'Uncontrollable sometimes. There was . . . oddness . . . in my husband's family. When I first came here she had to be sedated and locked in her room some days, and she would break furniture and throw things and scream hysterically. Then, after she . . .' She broke off, short of breath, and I saw tears in her eyes. I waited.

'She tried to burn down the house one night,' she said. 'The fire started in Adele's room—she was just a baby, but Bertha was very jealous of her at first.'

'You mean she tried to kill Adele?'

'No, of course not. She was just out of control. She isn't a murderer.' But I could see she believed otherwise.

'What happened?'

'She was sent away for a while, hospitalised. I believe there were drugs and electric shock treatment. She was much calmer when she came back. We dismissed Grace Poole then. But now . . . oh, my dear, I'm afraid she's jealous of you in just the same way.'

I was thinking, piecing things together. 'That's why she's been away,' I said slowly. 'She was having treatment again. Why? What had she done this time?'

'She hadn't done anything. But she was showing signs.' She obviously didn't want to go on, but I was ruthless that night.

'What signs?' I cast my mind back several months. Bertha had been irritable and restless. What else?

'You remember the kittens?' She twisted her hands in her lap.

'Adele's kittens? The ones that disappeared? And we thought the mother-cat had moved them because of all the fuss over them?'

'She strangled them.' She was sobbing. 'We had to bury them before Adele saw. We thought she was better—we thought it was safe to have animals here again.'

I realised now that apart from the old tabby there were no pets round the house, which was surely strange for a country homestead. From my reading, I knew that most had dogs and puppies and cats galore.

'Why?' I said again, it seemed to be all I could say. 'Why did she kill them?'

My aunt rubbed at her eyes. 'She hates Adele, didn't you realise? That's why Edward is so careful not to give the child any attention when Bertha's around. She's jealous of her, and she hates her to have anything she loves.'

I was quiet for a while. Things were slowly falling into place. 'And now she's jealous of me,'

I said. 'What will she do to me? Will she try to kill me, too?'

'Of course not.' She looked terrified suddenly, realising she had said far too much. 'Jane, I've wired Edward and told him he has to come home. I think she will have to be put away again. Apparently she was much better at the Ingrams', after the clinic. And Edward had hired Grace again ... It was a new treatment ... But it hasn't lasted.'

'No,' I said. 'Obviously not.'

'Oh God,' she said. 'I really thought she might be all right this time, and she seemed pleased about Edward and Blanche ...' she bit her lip; again she'd said more than she meant to.

I feel my heart begin to crack open.

Blanche Ingram, the one who had laughed at me and given me looks of amused contempt when she stayed here. Was she travelling with Edward now? She was beautiful. She was rich and she had a law degree which she didn't use, since she ran the station after her father's death. Edward's marrying her would mean joining the two properties, which shared fifty kilometres or so of boundary. I should have realised, I thought dully. She was so much more suitable than me.

I left the kitchen then, too dispirited to go on with my inquisition, too bound up in my own unhappiness to comfort my aunt. I went to my room, not bothering to lock the door. In fact, I felt that if Bertha did want to murder me, it might as well be tonight when it would almost be welcome.

As soon as Edward came back, I decided, I would leave. I couldn't face going away without seeing him one last time. I threw myself on my bed and gave way to a thorough fit of crying.

But I am not to be left in peace with my misery. The door opens softly, and Bertha comes in.

'Did you think he would marry *you*?' she said contemptuously. 'A little snip of nothing like you? Is your poor heart broken, now?' She must have been listening outside the kitchen window.

She sat beside me on the bed, crowding me into the corner. I was too exhausted to be frightened of her, though I thought she must have hated me knowing about her madness.

'He will never marry anyone without my

say-so,' she said, hissing the last words. 'Never.'

'Surely he'll make up his own mind,' I said weakly. 'I don't believe he'd just do what you tell him to.'

'Oh, he will. On this he will. He has to.' She began to laugh, shrilly, thrusting her face into mine.

'Did you really believe I was his sister? Did you? I am his legal wife. What do you think of that?'

I am beyond thinking, but somewhere the words register and make their own terrible sense.

It explained the way they treated each other, the way she watched him and goaded him, her terrible jealousy.

She began to gabble out the whole story, in between laughing and clutching at me. Now I was finding out more than I ever wanted to know. If I'd had any energy left I would have run away from her and her appalling narrative, away into the bush, but I was frozen, like a rabbit in a spotlight.

I can only sit, cowering, and listen.

They were second cousins, she explained. It had been almost an arranged marriage—she had the money and he had the property and the respectable name. I gathered her parents had been rackety and scandalous. She had only been sixteen when they married: 'He likes them young,' she said with her terrible cackle. And Adele—poor Adele—she was Bertha's child by another man, a man she had run off with once, in France. 'Did you think she was Edward's love child?' She leered at me. I didn't answer, but I suppose I had thought something like that. Bertha had abandoned the baby to an orphanage after the father left her, but Edward had found her and legally adopted her. Bertha hadn't wanted her found. 'Little brat. Stupid, like her father.'

She lost track of her story often, digressing into insults flung at me and my aunt, even Edward, but in the end I knew everything. Edward had taken Bertha back, after he found her on heroin in Berlin, frittering away her money on drugs and poor companions. He'd sent her to a clinic to dry out. She had refused to divorce him, although he was by then in love with another woman.

My heart cracks even wider.

It was Bertha who'd suggested they lie about

their relationship. If he would take her back and live with her, she said, she wouldn't stand in the way of his love affairs. Even in her demented state she had known she needed the security of a home and someone to look after her. 'Besides,' she said carelessly, 'the money was mine. He would have lost it if we'd divorced.'

By then I was ready to believe anything of him; it hardly mattered any more if he was shallow and mercenary as well as a liar.

'But you'd let him marry Blanche?' I managed to gasp out. 'You'd stand by for bigamy?'

'Oh yes,' she said. 'But only Blanche. We would be a threesome then, you understand?' She could see from my face that I didn't. 'Blanche is my lover, too, you little fool.' I struggled to understand her. It was the word 'too' that hurt me. Was Edward Blanche's lover? Had he been sneaking off to rendezvous with her all the while I had thought he was beginning to love me?

Bertha went on, now in a dreary monotone, but with glittering eyes, spewing filth at me, the details of her love for Blanche, the things they did together and with others. The things they would all three do when Blanche 'married'

Edward. Her hand began creeping up my arm; she seemed about to kiss me. I leapt off the bed, finally repelled out of my trance.

I run out and into my aunt's room, followed by Bertha's senseless laughter.

The next day Edward came home. I kept close to my great-aunt, who was, in fact, quite ill, and ignored his hints that he would like to talk to me. He had brought a doctor with him, who spent a while in Bertha's room, and came out shaking his head. I heard arrangements being made in low voices over the phone. It appeared someone would be fetching Bertha the next day.

I listened without shame on my aunt's extension. I knew everything up to now, I thought; I would know the rest as well. I heard Edward ringing one of the stockmen, arranging for Adele and Sophie to stay with his family for a few days.

Finally I went out and asked the doctor to look at Aunt Fairfax, who was grey and gasping on her bed. I stood by without emotion while he rang for an ambulance to take her to the local hospital, and without emotion I packed her things.

She holds out her hand to me as she leaves on a stretcher, but I pretend not to see. Later I find out that she died that night.

In the end, there was only Edward and me left to talk. Bertha, I assumed, had been sedated. I never said goodbye to Adele and Sophie, but watched from the window when they were picked up and driven away.

I feel I have been lied to and betrayed by everyone in that house.

But of course, Adele had not intended to deceive me. It is the only thing I feel remorse for, now, that I didn't kiss her goodbye.

He tracked me down to the library, where I sat huddled on the window seat.

He is carrying the first bud of a regenerated rose.

'I first saw you there,' he said, with a smile that went somehow awry. 'A funny little thing with books stockpiled around you as if they would go away if you didn't keep your eye on them.'

I said nothing, only looked at him.

'I'd like to tell you my side of it, Jane,' he said.

He holds out the rosebud and I take it.

'Don't bother,' I said. I had finally found some hardness in me, but it was fragile.

When he kneels beside me I collapse, weeping, and run my fingers through his hair.

'Why didn't you tell me the truth?' I said, through my tears. 'I loved you so much. I would have understood if you'd trusted me.'

He raises his face and kisses me, kisses that somehow also take away my tears.

'That's the trouble,' he said. 'You would have forgiven me anything. You would have given up your own life for me, Janie, and I'm not so far gone as to let you do that.'

'Tell me one thing,' I said. 'Did you . . . were you really beginning to love me, too?'

He looks over my shoulder at the garden and the paddocks stretching into the distance. 'Oh, yes,' he says.

'I had fantasies of starting all over again, with you, with something clean and new. But you can't start again, not when you're like me, when you've done so many things wrong already . . . The only good thing I could do was go away, leave you to get over it and make your own life . . .'

He stood up and went to the door. 'Jane, after tomorrow, when Bertha's gone, will you stay? Will you try to see if there's something we can build out of this?'

I think if even then he'd been straight enough to lay things out, to say we could be lovers but nothing more, I would have agreed. But something small and spiteful in me wasn't appeased.

'What about Blanche?' I said and saw him tighten his mouth.

I don't give him a chance to answer, to say it is all a mistake, or Bertha's lie, but run out of the room and into mine, where I lock the door. I shred the rose, petal by petal and drop it on the floor.

I heard him go out in the evening, and pace for a while on the verandah, waiting. Then I heard him walk off towards the stables, whistling sadly. I crept into the kitchen and made myself a sandwich, then I packed my things and went to bed.

I woke up in the cold, darkest hours of the morning. There was a smell of smoke and I immediately knew on some visceral level what was happening. I ran into the hall and saw that the other half of the house was full of flames. 'Edward,' I yelled and ran outside, intending to try to get to his room from the other entrance.

Then he is running from the stables—he must have been out riding all night; he is sweaty and smells of horses. He clutches me briefly and gives me a wild kiss.

'You're all right,' he said. 'Thank God.'

'It must have started in Adele's room,' I said. 'Again.' Bertha wouldn't have known Adele wasn't there.

He looked at me, and I saw the thought come into his head. 'Bertha? She's still inside!' he said.

I see his next thought, too, and I share it. I walk away without saying anything, away from the leaping orange flames of the house, down to the lily pond where the moonlight still casts a silvery patina over the water, and I sit on the stone bench there, my mind deliberately empty.

When the cars and trucks began to arrive from the nearest huts, I got up and slowly walked back to the house. Bertha lay on the lawn, obviously dead from smoke inhalation, and Edward stood near her, his expression unreadable.

'I tried to get her out,' he says to me, almost as if he was rehearsing it. 'I did try.' I turn away and watch the powerful hoses scattering in the sudden gale that springs up out of nowhere. The newly budding roses are drowned and trampled, broken into the ground.

Now I live alone, in Sydney, in a small terrace house, with my cats. All these things happened not so very long ago, exactly ten years, in fact, but it seems a lifetime. Edward married Blanche, eventually, as I knew he would. I see their photographs sometimes in the society pages and he looks old and unhappy, grimly doing the rounds of the balls and the charity dinners. She looks triumphant.

I haven't married. I've never even kissed another man. Whenever I've felt tempted, I've looked into their eager, lying faces and wondered what cesspools of intrigue they are concealing.

For a while I thought of going back to Lowood—I have returned to the Bible and the true word of God. But then the newspaper articles starting appearing, about the drugs and orgies, and I realised there was no salvation there. I don't go to church—Lowood destroyed forever any faith in religion interpreted by others. I work in the local library, a job I was lucky to get, with no training. My inheritance was enough to buy this little house. I changed my name so that no one from my past could come after me, and I've kept myself to myself.

I've made no friends. I see them in the library, people who seem friendly, and I feel I know already what they are like underneath—dishonest and self-serving. I don't even feel the need to prove myself wrong.

It is ten years to the day that I left Thornfield and my accomplice in murder. I feel no remorse, except towards Adele, who must now be the same age I was when I went to Thornfield. I feel for her, parentless, probably shunted away to some uncaring boarding school. I've left this house and my money to be shared between her and Reed. I've long forgiven Reed everything—in her way she was as honest a person as I've ever known.

I've put a note in my neighbour's letter-box, asking her to look after the cats. I'll let them out in a minute, before I take the pills. I've read the Bible from cover to cover, and I can find nowhere that we are forbidden to do this. Another false interpretation by false prophets.

Now I put my trust in the only one who has never betrayed it:

'Surely I come quickly,' says Christ.

I eagerly respond, 'Amen, even so come, Lord Jesus.'

LOVE'S DARK FACE

THE LETTERS OF JEAN RHYS

Ella Gwendolyn Rees Williams—Jean Rhys—was born in August 1890 in Dominica in the British West Indies. As a teenager she left for England to be educated, studying at the Royal Academy of Dramatic Art until her father's death forced her to support herself. After touring in the chorus of a musical comedy company, she later took jobs as a model, tutor and translator. Her first short story collection was published in 1927 as *The Left Bank and Other Stories* and praised by Ford Madox Ford for the author's 'passion for stating the case of the underdog'. In the 1920s and '30s Rhys wrote four novels—*Quartet, After Leaving Mr Mackenzie, Voyage in the Dark* and *Good Morning, Midnight* before disappearing from sight. When the BBC produced a radio version of *Good Morning, Midnight* in 1957, interest in her work was rekindled, and Rhys was discovered living in Devon. She worked on *Wide Sargasso Sea*—a prequel to Charlotte Brontë's *Jane Eyre* told from the viewpoint of Rochester's first wife—for many years before it was published in 1966 to critical acclaim. With the resurgence of feminism in the 1970s, Jean Rhys's pioneering work in portraying the difficulties of single women in a male-dominated society was recognised.

TO FRANCIS WYNDHAM*

April 14th [1964]
Cheriton Fitz Paine

Dear Mr Wyndham,

... I am now so taken up with *Sargasso Sea* that I am proud to say that I've got writer's cramp—must be the only person in the world who has it—what with typists, tape recorders

* Francis Wyndham, an editor at the publishing house André Deutsch, became a friend and mentor of Jean Rhys in 1957 after hearing a dramatisation of *Good Morning, Midnight* on the BBC and writing to her.

and so on. Isn't *that* something? I have to write carefully though—to be legible which slows me up (still more).

I am in touch with Miss Athill who wrote me the kindest of letters.* There's a typewriting firm next door, she says, who can manage what I send—so that's *one* problem solved.

Now about the book—I was rather down with this and that, so flew to writing poems. This I've always done (aged 12 or 10 when I started). They are strewn all over the places I've lived in—didn't keep many. I like some of them and can do them quickly.

Well I wrote four. The best, I think, is called 'The Old Man's Home' but it's the one I enclose which gave me the clue to my book. (Please remember that what I write helps me—written clearly or not it helps. So don't be bored.) A struggle with my handwriting plus writer's cramp. Still—It is quite true that I've brooded over *Jane Eyre* for years.

The Brontë sisters had of course a touch of

---

* Diana Athill, Jean's editor at André Deutsch, who treated her with kindness and patience and was rewarded with a masterpiece.

genius (or much more) especially Emily. So reading *Jane Eyre* one's swept along regardless. But *I*, reading it later, and often, was vexed at her portrait of the 'paper tiger' lunatic, the all wrong creole scenes, and above all by the real cruelty of Mr Rochester. After all, he was a very wealthy man and there were many kinder ways of disposing of (or hiding) an unwanted wife—I heard the true story of one—and the man behaved very differently. (Another clue.)

Even when I knew I *had* to write the book—still it did not click into place—that is one reason (though only one) why I was so long. It didn't click. It wasn't there. However I tried.

Only when I wrote this poem—then it clicked—and all was there and always had been.

The first clue is Obeah which I assure you existed, and still does, in Haiti South America and of course in Africa—under different names. The others—*sais pas*. It was against the law in the 'English' islands. The second clue was when Miss Athill suggested a few weeks of happiness for the unfortunate couple—before he gets disturbing letters. As soon as I wrote that bit I realised that he must have fallen for her—and violently too. The black people have or had a good word for it—'she *magic* with him' or 'he *magic* with her'. Because you see, that is what it is—magic, intoxication. Not 'Love' at all. There is too the magic of the place, which is not all lovely beaches or smiling people—it can be a very disturbing kind of beauty. Many people have felt that and written about it too. So poor Mr R, being in this state gets this letter and is very unhappy indeed.

Now is the time for Obeah. The poor (she too) girl doesn't know *why* he's so suddenly left her in the lurch, so flies off to her nurse (presence explained) for a love drink. From the start it must be made clear that Christophine is 'an obeah woman'. When her, Antoinette's (rather confused) explanations fall flat, she slips him the love drink. *At once*. That is the only change to be made. It must be *at once*.

In obeah these drinks or sacrifices or whatever have this effect: The god himself enters the person who has drunk. Afterwards he (or she) faints, recovers, and remembers very little of what has happened (they say). I wouldn't know.

Not Mr R. He remembers *everything* including the fact that he has felt a bit uneasy in the early happy days and asked her to tell him what's wrong, promised to believe her, and stand by her, and she's always answered 'Nothing is wrong'. For, poor child, she is *afraid* to tell him, and cries if he insists.

So he strides into her bedroom, not himself, but angry love and that is what the poem is about.

Even when the love has gone the anger is still there and remains. (No obeah needed for that!) And remains.

Well this is now a long letter. Have you got so far? *Continuez*—

Mr Rochester tries hard not to be a tyrant. Back in Spanish Town he gives her a certain freedom, *tries* to be kindly if distant.

But now she is angry too. Like a hurricane. Like a Creole. For his second revenge—his affair with her maid (and next door) has hurt more than the first.

She uses her freedom to rush off and have an affair too—first with her pal Sandi—then with others. All coloured or black, which was, in those days, a *terrible* thing for a white girl to do. Not to be forgiven. The men did as they liked. The women—*never*.

So imagine Mr R's delight when he can haul

her to England, lock her up in a cold dark room, deprive her of all she's used to—watch her growing mad. And so on—I think the governess and the house party rash. But I suppose he thought her fini by that time. Well, she wasn't—

I think there were several Antoinettes and Mr Rochesters. Indeed I am sure. Mine is *not* Miss Brontë's, though much suggested by *Jane Eyre*. She is, to start with, young not old. She is still a girl when she fires the house and jumps to her death. And hates last. Mr R's name ought to be changed. Raworth? A Yorkshire name isn't it? The sound is right. In the poem (if it's that) Mr Rochester (or Raworth) consoles himself or justifies himself by saying that *his* Antoinette runs away after the 'Obeah nights' and that the creature who comes back is not the one who ran away. I wish this had been thought of before—for that too is part of Obeah.

A Zombie is a dead person raised up by the Obeah woman, it's usually a woman I think, and a zombie can take the appearance of anyone. Or anything.

But I did not write it that way and I'm glad, for it would have been a bit creepy! And probably, certainly I think, beyond me.

Still, it's a thought—for anyone who writes those sort of stories.

No. Antoinette herself comes back but so changed that perhaps she *was* 'lost Antoinette'. I insist that she must be lovely, and certainly she was lost. 'All in the romantic tradition'.

As for what I've done—the time when 'she magic for him'. The letter—better and shorter. The interview with Daniel. That's all for Part II. The end when they leave for Spanish Town. Also most of the corrections and cuts and the *first chapter rewritten. Important* as it explains Christophine in Grandbois.

It's all a bit of a scrawl but I can do it and know it. It is done except Part III.

Yes I need a holiday, *short*, but I feel that perhaps I'd better get it straight here. I have solitude and privacy—both not so easy to get and there's rather a good tree to look at. I'm sure the neighbours think I'm potty but after all—they can hardly haul me off to the bin for scribble scribble scribble. Quite noiselessly. I really believe that if I had a typewriter they would, for I work late now. (They don't like books much.)

I must post this and the one to Miss Athill. So that is all for now and enough too. The return to Spanish Town and Sandi have been *implied* not written about directly. All along.

Sincerely yours,
Jean Rhys

OBEAH NIGHT

A night I seldom remember
(If it can be helped)
The night I saw Love's dark face
Was Love's dark face
'And cruel as he is'? I've never known that
I tried my best you may be certain
(whoever asks)
My human best

If the next morning as I looked at what I'd done
(He was watching us mockingly, used to these games)
If I'd stared back at him
If I'd said
'I was a god myself last night
I've tamed and changed a wild girl'
Or taken my hurt darling in my arms
(Conquered at last. And silent. Mine)

Perhaps Love would have smiled then
Shown us the way
Across the sea. They say it's strewn with
wrecks
And weed-infested
Few dare it, fewer still escape
But *we*, led by smiling Love
We could have sailed
Reached a safe harbour
Found a sweet, brief heaven
Lived our short lives

But I was both sick and sad
(Night always ends)
She was a stranger
Wearing the mask of pain
Bearing the marks of pain—
I turned away—Traitor
Too sane to face my madness (or despair)
Far, far too cold and sane

Then Love, relenting
Sent clouds and soft rain
Sent sun, light and shadow
To show me again
Her young face waiting

Waiting for comfort and a gentler lover?
(You'll not find him)
A kinder loving? *Love is not kind*
I would not look at her
(Once is enough)
Over my dead love
Over a sleeping girl
I drew a sheet
Cover the stains of tears
Cover the marks of blood
(You can say nothing
That I have not said a thousand times and one
Excepting this—That night was Something Else
I was Angry Love Himself
Blind fierce avenging Love—no other that night)

'It's too strong for Béké'
The black woman said
Love, hate or jealousy
Which had she seen?
She knew well—the *Devil*!
—What it could mean

How can I forget you Antoinette
When the spring is here?
Where did you hide yourself

After that shameless, shameful night?
And why come back? Hating and hated?
Was it Love, Fear, Hoping?
Or (as always) Pain?
(*Did* you come back I wonder
Did I ever see you again?)

No. I'll lock that door
Forget it.—
The motto was 'Locked Hearts I open
I have the heavy key'
Written in black letters
Under a Royal Palm Tree
On a slave owner's gravestone
'Look! And look again, hypocrite' he says
'Before *you* judge *me*'

I'm no damn slave owner
I have no slave
Didn't she (forgiven) betray me
Once more—and then again
Unrepentant—laughing?

I can soon show her
Who hates the best
Always she answers me
I will hate last

Lost, lovely Antoinette
How can I forget you
When the spring comes?
(Spring is cold and furtive here
There's a different rain)
Where did you hide yourself
After the obeah nights?
(*What* did you send instead?
Hating and hated?)
Where did you go?
I'll never see you now
I'll never know
For you left me—my truest Love
Long ago

Edward Rochester or Raworth
Written in Spring 1842

TO DIANA ATHILL

April 28th [1964]
Cheriton Fitz Paine

It's not 'Stormy Weather' I'm thinking
of now. It's 'You'll take the high road
And I'll take the low road
But I'll be in Scotland before you.'
Why? Don't know.

Dear Diana,

I wrote you two long letters which I won't send for they are the same old song once again and what's the use?

I do not quite understand why, when *I* have told you that this book is finished (in my scrawl and a kind of shorthand I've invented) but finished (but for part III—short) you reply No *they* say it's unfinished. What *They?* and *Why?* However there are so many puzzling matters. So let's pass on. I think that in all the muddle two things stick out five miles.

The first one is that for several years (YEARS) I could not really work at this romantic novel (my first Romance) because my husband fell seriously ill not long after I started. Max is not a bundle of old rags to me—he is Max. (Nice too. Was. A stoic) But though torn in two I still worked and bluffed as well. At night. On pep pills. So at last the *Skeleton* was there. Then I got it typed with some difficulty you bet! *Got in one exit shot tho* at Madame Brown. Also *Monsieur* B, and so on—

When Max (who is a very important factor in all this), though he is, let's say, a *hidden* factor, disregarded, went into hospital I spent some bad weeks of loneliness and near despair. This is a lonely place.

Then I said '*Come On*' and '*Steady does it*' as my long dead PA said and started on Part II. Part I (a third of the book) was (I thought) finished—or nearly—additions corrections et al and in safe hands. But now I sometimes wonder—what *has* become of Part I and *needed* additions? *Don't* say it's lost stolen or strayed? 'Or I shall weep. Then sleep Five fathoms deep. Nor ever rise' (quotation from Book).

I won't harrow you with my struggles. Damned old Part II!! Never mind—Rot chucked out, Bits put in. Even spelling fixed up. Still it was (to me) dead as a dead heart. Not all of course. So I remembered what I'd been told by one of these old hat lot who after all *knew their job* and something about writing and *writers* and all that Jazz and what one *feels* (which is also important). PUT IT AWAY I was told. *Do something Else.* So I did. Part II was put away and I worked on four poems. [. . .] Well, after second poem came what I call the *Breakthrough* and I saw what was wrong and why it (the book) was dead. I'd got the girl (less or more) but my Mr R was *all wrong*. Also a *heel*. First, he coldly marries a girl for her dough, *then* he believes everything he's told about her, finally he drags her to England, shuts her up in a cold dark room for *years* and brings sweet little Janey to look at the result—this noble character! Noble!! My God! As soon as I saw that it all came to life. It had always been there . . . Mr Rochester is *not* a heel. He is a fierce and violent (Heathcliff) man who marries an alien creature, partly because his father arranges it, partly because he has had a bad attack of fever, partly no doubt for *lovely* mun, but most of all because he is *curious* about this girl—already half in love.

Then (this is good old Part II) they get to this lovely lonely magic place and there is no 'half' at all. My Mr Rochester as I see him becomes as fierce as Heathcliff and as jealous as Othello. He is also a bit uneasy (not used to strong magic at all). *Suspicious*—(*Why do I feel like this?*) (That you see is where I went so wrong.) Well this is what I've done—as the letter is becoming a long letter and tedious. Not much is *changed. A lot is written in and done. All done.*

I have tried to show this man being magicked by the place which is (or was) a lovely, lost *and magic* place but, if you understand, a *violent* place. (Perhaps there is violence in *all* magic and *all* beauty—but there—very strong) magicked by the girl—the two are mixed up perhaps to bewildered English gent, Mr R, certain that she's hiding something from him. And of course she *is*. Her mad mother. (Not mad perhaps at all) So you see—when he gets this letter all blows sky high. And so—I've fixed up the letter, written in his interview with Daniel whom Mr R detests but believes. (Why) I could guess that too I think—because he *wants* to—that's why. Also that awful bastard Daniel has persuaded him that his wife is not only mad but plain *bad*. Sandi and others. So you see—poor Mr Rochester—and poor lovely Antoinette too. She runs away to Christophine but comes back for she also is now desperately in love. (*Of course!*) I have written in a long interview with Christophine but the end of interview remains as before—nearly. The last chapter when they leave I will send to you. It is part 'poetry' part prose. It *may* be fustian (I think not) but can be altered easily enough to prose. *Not Now*. As I told you the *MSS* is not altered (much. *Some wasn't too right you know*). The *slant* has been altered. It is not so tame—that's all. Additions do it.

Oh yes I've cut out the vomiting and so on and made it that the 'love' drink on Obeah Night merely releases all the misery, jealousy and ferocity that has been piling up in Mr R for so long. He pretends to think he's been poisoned—that's only to pile up (again) everything he can against her and so excuse his cruelty. He *justifies* it that way. (It's often done)

I do not think that it *justifies* him at all. I *do* think it *explains* him a bit. However (—So *cold* before he was). If when it is done you do not like it—then say so. No problem. All will be arranged. Cash etc.

But it's always *trust* or it'll go *bust*. This I got from a very wealthy man long ago, I've had a *rum* life! who (*en passant*) was explaining J P Morgan's intimate affairs. *Why?* That's gone. Me listening to all this not getting the point at all really. But he said 'When you are dealing with *Big Money* you've *got* to trust the other chap sometimes—or the whole dam thing would collapse.' Something like that. I've remembered enough to have '*Trust* or go *bust*' firmly fixed in my erratic head. Well Books can be Big too. Or small. Or nothing. (The writer doesn't matter at all—he is only the instrument. But . . . he must not be smashed. Or *he* goes bust. Then no music if you smash the violin.)

Well please believe that I am doing my best. I have waited long for the Breakthrough trusting trusting it would come and it has now. I think. *No more slow painful stuff. Quick now. You will have it by summer.*

I heard from Christy & Moore this morning—thank you.

Beautiful Dough.

Why do I love you so?

Indeed I feel a lot better already. A bit tired lately (said the crying child). I like *that* too.

But all this *write write all night* and food such a bore—

Not so-o good. Now comes the time to trust or I'll bust. Which is point no. 2. That is the danger. (*I think not bust though.*)

Mrs Whitby* was and will be an enormous help. *So* nice. But give me a little time to fix up flat and my battered self. Also to get the stuff straight, and no fumbling. Or losing Bits. I will make it all shipshape & Bristol fashion. Meantime give her my best thanks past and to come. It's Stormy Weather here. But must stop sometime, surely.

Yours what you will,
Jean

TO FRANCIS WYNDHAM

Thursday [1964]
Cheriton Fitz Paine

Dear Mr Wyndham,

... I realise what I lose by cutting loose from Jane Eyre and Mr Rochester—Only too well. (Indeed *can* I?) Names? Dates?

* Esther Whitby, an editor from Deutsch, came to Jean Rhys's home in August 1963 and typed the manuscript of *Wide Sargasso Sea*.

But I believe and firmly too that there was more than one Antoinette. The West Indies was (were?) rich in those days *for* those days and there was no 'married woman's property Act'. The girls (very tiresome no doubt) would soon once in kind England be *Address Unknown*. So gossip. So a legend. If Charlotte Brontë took her horrible Bertha from this legend I have the right to take lost Antoinette. And, how to reconcile the two and fix dates I do not know—yet. But, I will. Another thing is this:—

I have a very great and deep admiration for the Brontë sisters (Though Charlotte did preachify sometimes). (And all the rest.) And often boring perhaps. (Me too!)

How then can *I* of all people, say she was wrong? Or that her Bertha is impossible? *Which she is*. Or get cheap publicity from her (often) splendid book?

She wrote: —Charlotte did: 'This I know: The writer ... owns something of which he is not always master ... it will perhaps for years lie in subjection ... then without warning of revolt there comes a time ... when it sets to work ... You have little choice left but quiescent adoption (?) As for you, the *nominal* artist—your share is to work passively—under dictates you neither delivered nor could question—that would not be delivered at your prayer, nor changed at your caprice. If the result be attractive the World will praise you, who little deserve praise. If it be repulsive the World will blame you, who as little deserve blame.'

So you see she *knew*. It is so. And it is so. (As for Emily—well less said about her the better. Hope Mr W S gave her a drink and a big kiss.* In Valhalla.)

I will try—I have this book now. A lot is in poetry which I'll carefully turn into prose. Or perhaps not all prose. I too 'little deserve praise or blame'. (Sometimes) If I have been long—well it has been harder than you know. Or would believe perhaps.

I think you have been most generous to me, encouraged me when I'd nearly given up, helped me when I needed help. But a bit bored sometimes—Not? A bit impatient and *why doesn't*

---

* Probably William Shakespeare, according to Francis Wyndham.

this woman hurry up for God's sake? And why bother me any more? Not??

Well it's all hard and lonely. And remember that *This* can force you to try to use others *almost* tho' not nearly as relentlessly as you are obliged to use yourself. But now comes the let up, and the breakthrough and no more asking for help from anyone—Or boring anybody. However understanding and merciful.

I will finish this book by myself and be passive and write what I am told to write. I don't care any more what happens to it—once written. If it swims and does not sink then I will ask you to write a preface. Please. For perhaps you can put into words what I cannot. After all I don't know many words so have to use them carefully. I *always* know what is wrong—it often takes me a *long* time to get it right. See? All the same ...

... I feel a bit of an automaton now, which is no doubt part of it. The only thing is I can't sleep so sit up to all hours. It's late now. I must get it all in for I'll write no more long letters. I have not the right to worry anybody any more.

Never say or think—'I wish I'd left this

terrible creature alone.' Really! ... Because you see if I had not had this book, this hope—Of *What? Not dough*—these years would have been very tough. Too tough I think. Even for me. This is a very serious letter but I write jokey ones too. Fall a bit flat. But *I* laugh. I laughed over the '*Do you wish to be a Mental Giant? Easy Terms. Fill up Enclosed Form*' that circular for days. I *can't* learn that in England business is no joke. No joking either ... Oh dear—does so remind me of 'You know me? I was the one who laughed at your one line. Heard every word. Come on cheer up and have a drink.' (*I long and long for that*).

... I have no telephone and the village one (automatic) has (thank God) *Out of Order* on it and never will have anything else. Even the post box is miles away and I go to it singing in the rain. I do *not* think! Only my book matters. *Nothing but that*. Well last long letter, my hand and seal on it.

Yours sincerely and gratefully,

Jean Rhys

I will not crack. Sometimes I can write. In my twenties fashion. *And After too*.

How about

'*There comes a time*' for title

The *poem* ties up with 'Sargasso Sea' but with very little in the book. It's not important.

Yet.

I will send everything to Miss Athill. Even though I've heard nothing about Part I. Or additions. I expect it's in the dust bin—Or lost. Oh Well! *Bon Dieu!*

Don't you think I am being penalised rather heavily because I can't rattle away on a type-writer? And live in this impossible place? Perhaps not—I don't know.

I will finish my lament for Antoinette (and many others). Then I will ask Alec to come down though he doesn't care for Cheriton Fitz (*Who would?*) I will rest a little then come to lovely kind London. For the money you sent is there to be used for that.

Nothing but that.

Merci and thank you for so much.

J.R.

Very much.

TO DIANA ATHILL

February 15th [1966]
Cheriton Fitz Paine

My dear Diana,

This morning I had a letter from the Royal Literary Fund. They sent me a cheque for £300, and will give me this yearly for five years.

... Now I want to talk about the book for a while. I am working on the last bit—the end.

Sometimes I have to force myself but I do force myself.

I have this idea that all difficulties can be solved, and all put right by *cutting*—in fact I nearly wrote to you and suggested cutting all Part III, ending it in Jamaica and calling it Prelude to Thornton House or Thornfield or whatever. But that won't do.

So I will struggle on and try to make it as convincing as possible.

I can see it all up to a point. I mean a man *might* come to England with a crazy wife. He *might* leave her in charge of a housekeeper and a nurse and dash away to Europe. She *might* be treated far more harshly than he knows and so get madder and madder. He *might* funk seeing her when he returns. But really, to give a house party in the same house—I can't believe that. But then I've never believed in Charlotte's lunatic, that's why I wrote this book and really what a *devil* it's been.

Don't take all this too seriously. I do feel a bit light headed as I told you.

I hope to send you Part III by the end of this month. When you send me the typescript I'll go through the whole book. There's an addition in Part I, some deletes in Part II but No additions and No chapters.

Then it will be really ready as it should have been from the first of course.

Yours,

Jean

The answer is delete house party. Well I will as far as possible.

It's got quite dark while I've been writing this so can't post it till tomorrow.

TO DIANA ATHILL

Sunday 20th [1966]
Cheriton Fitz Paine

My dear Diana,

... Now about my book. I have finished it and will post the last part to be typed early next week—if you let me have one copy I'll put the whole thing together.

Please read this some time, though I always imagine you very busy.

I came to England between sixteen and seventeen, a very impressionable age and *Jane Eyre* was one of the books I read then.

Of course Charlotte Brontë makes her own world, of course she convinces you, and that makes the poor Creole lunatic all the more dreadful. I remember being quite shocked, and when I re-read it rather annoyed. 'That's only one side—the English side' sort of thing.

(I think too that Charlotte had a 'thing' about the West Indies being rather sinister places—because in another of her books *Villette* she drowns the hero, Professor Somebody, on the voyage to Guadeloupe, another very alien place—according to her.)

Perhaps most people had this idea then, and

perhaps in a way they were right. Even now white West Indians can be a bit trying—a bit very (not only white ones) but not quite so awful surely. They have a side and a point of view.

Well years and *years* afterwards the idea came to me to write this book.

I started off quite lightheartedly thinking I could do it easily, but I soon found out that it was going to be a *devil*, partly because I haven't much imagination really. I do like a basis of fact. I went on—sometimes blindly.

Part I was not too hard, but by Part II I'd quite abandoned the idea of *Jane Eyre*.

There were many unfortunate marriages at that time and before—West Indian planters and merchants were wealthy before sugar crashed—and their daughters were very good matches.

Some of the owners stayed in England and managed their estates through agents, but some didn't. Perhaps you know all this.

Well this was the story of one arranged marriage, with the bridegroom young, *unwilling*, rather suspicious and ready to believe the worst, not liking the semi tropics at all, and the bride poor bride very romantic, with some French or Spanish blood, perhaps with the seeds of madness, at any rate hysteria. The most seriously wrong thing with Part II is that I've made the obeah woman, the nurse, too articulate. I thought of cutting it a bit, I will if you like, but after all no one will notice. Besides there's no reason why one particular negro woman shouldn't be articulate enough, especially as she's spent most of her life in a white household.

So I only borrowed the name Antoinette—(I carefully haven't named the man at all) and the idea of her seeming a bit mad—to an Englishman.

Of course with Part III, I'm right back with the plot of *Jane Eyre*, leaving out Jane! I didn't know how else to end it. I didn't even know how to explain their entirely changed life, England not the West Indies, quite mad instead of a bit strange. I thought the best way out was to do it at once through Grace Poole. It *could* be done by putting it in the third person but perhaps that would lose something. I rather shiver at the idea of doing it *again*, but I will if you tell me that it would gain a lot in clarity. By it I mean Part III.

It wouldn't take long—it's casting about

trying this way and that—takes the time. And the worry.

I mean all the action to take place between 1834 and 1845 say. *Quick*. My Antoinette marries very young, and when she is brought to England and shut up isn't much over twenty. Her confinement doesn't last long. She burns the house and kills herself (bravo!) very soon. I think she would become first a legend, then a monster, quickly. Charlotte may or may not have heard the legend but that is guesswork and impertinent because really I don't know.* Now I must end this monstrous letter which please read when you're in the mood.

Yrs,
Jean
Thank you Diana.

* Charlotte Brontë had indeed heard a 'legend'. According to Lyndall Gordon in 'A Public Voice', in 1845 she visited the Eyre family seat of North Lees, where the first mistress of the house reputedly went insane, was locked in a padded room upstairs, and died by fire.

TO DIANA ATHILL

Wednesday March 9th [1966]
Cheriton Fitz Paine

My dear Diana,

Thank you for your letter. I don't know what else to say. Max died unconscious, and this morning very early we went to the Exeter crematorium.

A sunny day, a *cold* sun, and a lot of flowers but it made no sense to me.

I feel that I've been walking a tight rope for a long, long time and have finally fallen off. I can't believe that I am so alone, and that there is no Max.

I've dreamt several times that I was going to have a baby—then I woke with relief.

Finally I dreamt that I was looking at the baby in a cradle—such a puny weak thing.

So the book must be finished, and that must be what I think about it really. I don't dream about it any more.

I am sorry for a sad letter and I send you my love.

Jean

It's so *cold*.

Francis Wyndham and Diana Melly ended this collection of Jean Rhys's letters on a note of death and birth. In this last letter Jean informs Diana of her husband's death, but also recounts the dream that had made her realise she'd finally won the long struggle to finish *Wide Sargasso Sea*. It is intriguing that both Jean Rhys and Jane Eyre dreamed of infants at crisis points in their lives. The novel was published seven months later, in October 1966, and was an outstanding critical success, winning the Society of Literature and the W.H. Smith Awards as well as a lasting reputation as a minor masterpiece.